THE GATLING GUN NOTEBOOK

A COLLECTION OF DATA and ILLUSTRATIONS

Gatling Guns, Component Parts,
Nomenclature, Mounts,
Ammunition and Accessories,
Makers, Users and Serial Numbers

Compiled By James B. Hughes
From Contemporary Sources

LIBRARY OF CONGRESS
CATALOG CARD NO.: 00-134303
    James B. Hughes
        The Gatling Gun Notebook
    Lincoln, RI: ANDREW MOWBRAY INCORPORATED — Publishers
        152 pp.

ISBN: 0-917218-94-9

To order additional copies of this book, call 1-800-999-4697.

Printed in the United States of America.

1   2   3   4   5   6   7   8   9   10

This history of the Gatling Gun
Is respectfully dedicated to
Those men whose ideas and
Inventive genius created this
Fascinating "machine gun,"
Long obsolete but still
Of interest to Collectors,
Researchers, and Historians
Everywhere…the
Story lives on…

James B. Hughes

TABLE OF CONTENTS

INTRODUCTION

The Gatling Gun was the first successful "machine gun;" however, it was not a true machine gun. The power to operate the gun was provided by the arm of the gunner.

The first six Gatling Guns were built during November and December 1862. The maker was the Miles Greenwood Foundry & Machine Works of Cincinnati, Ohio. Before they were delivered, the factory, patterns and guns were destroyed by a fire. Production resumed at the Cincinnati Type Foundry during 1863. Thirteen Gatlings were assembled there. Early in 1866, production was moved to the Cooper Firearms Manufacturing Company in Philadelphia, Pennsylvania. Later in 1866, all American production was transferred to Colt's Patent Fire Arms Manufacturing Company, of Hartford, Connecticut.

Colt's established the Gatling Gun Company as a sales arm for this "machine gun" during 1866. This company lasted until 1909. Until 1874, they had a Sales Office at 24½ East Washington Street, Indianapolis, Indiana. When R.J. Gatling moved to Hartford, this office was closed and the Gatling Gun Company was reincorporated in Connecticut. The inventor served as president of the sales company until 1897.

The term "Machine Gun" or "Battery Gun" was used by Gatling, Colt, the United States and foreign Patent Offices, and all contemporary writers and military men. Later, the true machine gun was described as an "automatic machine gun" to distinguish it from the manually operated forerunners.

The data and illustrations were taken from contemporary sources published in the United States and Europe. Your author apologizes for the uneven quality of the line drawings used to illustrate the Gatling Guns and their related accessories and ammunition. However, many were copied from crumbling, yellowed paper. Most are over 100 years old. They are the best that could be found to achieve my goal of illustrating this book using only "antique drawings." This effort has taken several years to accomplish.

This project began in 1972, as a notebook for my own reference. As I found these old line drawings and data in magazine articles, reports, books, etc., they were entered into my notebook for future reference. As the contents grew, I thought that this accumulation of Gatling Gun information should be shared with others interested in these weapons. This book is the result.

James B. Hughes
Houston, Texas
U.S.A.

AMERICAN-MADE GATLING GUN MODELS:

Year   *Model Name and Description/Notes*

1862   **First MODEL 1862:**
6 manufactured
.58 percussion, 6 barrels
Sale Price: $1,500 each
Mount: Field carriage
Destroyed by fire at factory
Second MODEL 1862:
13 manufactured
.58 Rimfire w/carrier, 6 barrels
Wedge locked
Sale Price: $1,000 each
U.S. Major General Benjamin Butler purchased 12
U.S. Admiral David D. Porter purchased 1
Mount: Field carriage

1865   **MODEL 1865:**
.58 Rimfire, 6 barrels
Mount: Field carriage

1866   **MODEL 1866:**
6 barrels
Introduced 1"
Mount: Field carriage
U.S. Major General Winfield Scott Hancock purchased 12
Improved MODEL 1866:
.50-70 introduced
Most with 6 barrels, a few with 10 barrels
Steel breech housing
Arched frame front introduced during production
Weights: 1" = 1,008 lbs., .50-70 = 224 lbs.
Mount: Field carriage
U.S. Army Contract: August 24, 1866, for 50 in 1", 50 in .50-70, manufactured by
    Colt's, delivery in 1867.
Also U.S. Navy contract for 22 x .50-70 Improved Model 1866 Gatlings

1871   **MODEL 1871:**
10 x .50-70 barrels; 5 or 6 at purchaser's request
Bolts made heavier and supporting rib added
Service "trapdoor" in breech casing to permit bolt removal
Broadwell 400-round drum magazine introduced
Broadwell "all-metal" carriage introduced
Curved magazine introduced as standard
Automatic oscillator (traversing mechanism) introduced
Mount: Field carriage

NOTE: Last Model 1866 1" gun made at Colt's, No. 121

1873   Few .50-70 guns manufactured, last models with angled feed hopper and center-located sights

1874   **MODEL 1874:**

10 x 32" .45-70 barrels

Introduced the .45-70 chambering

Only model with a folding front sight

Front and Rear sights moved to right side of gun

Bolts and breech housing shortened

Improved oscillator, feed hopper, magazine, headspace adjustment, main shaft

Crank lock added, for safety during headspace adjustment via set screw

Few guns accepted either Broadwell drum or Model 1874 magazine

Both serial numbers, which run from 1 upwards, and assembly numbers, which start at 1 each year, appear on guns

U.S. Navy serial numbers appear on top of barrel jacket

Weight: 200 lbs. (Army model) also reported to be 210 lbs.

Mount: Field carriage with improved oscillating mechanism

MODEL 1874 Camel Gun:

10 x 18" barrels

Weight: 135 lbs.

Mounts: Cavalry Cart, Tripod or Camel Saddles

Manufactured 1874–1876

1875   **MODEL 1875:**

Fixed (non-folding) Front Sight

Bolt faces beveled

Higher walls on feed hopper to support magazine better

A special U.S. Navy Model 1875 was produced with barrels longer than those of the Camel Gun, but shorter than the standard. This Navy contract introduced the bronze barrel jacket and a lightweight naval carriage

1876   **MODEL 1876:**

Cartridge hopper moved from left side to center of gun

Cartridge guides added

Bolt bevel improved

Quantity of interior beech casing screws increased

Lock for headspace adjustment washer added

1877   **MODEL 1877:**

New feed hopper to improve feeding

Higher rate of fire via faster pitch to gears

Last guns fitted with the Model 1874 cam-operated oscillator

MODEL 1877 Bulldog:

5 x 18" .45-70 barrels (10 barrels optional)

Rear-mounted crank, on main shaft

Barrel jacket became a standard feature

Headspace adjustment via nut on main shaft, which also retained crank

Windage adjustable front sight and trunnions cast integral with barrel jacket
Rear sight now adjustable for elevation on cascabel plate
Mechanical oscillating device, found only on this model, last one produced
Weight: 90 lbs.
Mounts: Tripod as standard, Cavalry Cart and field carriage

1879 MODEL 1879:
10 x 32" .45-70 barrels
Introduced "flexible yoke" with Aiming Bar
Trunnions moved towards breech to accommodate above, improving balance
Headspace adjustment moved from muzzle to breech, at cascabel knob, with spring lock
Weight: 200 lbs.
Mounts: Field carriage as standard, a few with Tripods
Note: Production may have begun during 1878

1881 MODEL 1881:
Bruce Feed introduced
Mouth of feed hopper adapted to above feed device
Last "exposed barrel" Gatlings sold to U.S. until 1889

1883 MODEL 1883:
10 x 32" .45-70 barrels, bronze barrel jacket
Accles Drum Feed introduced, 104 rounds of .45-70
Left Sights: .45-70-405
Right Sights: .45-70-500
Spirit Levels, parallel and perpendicular to barrels
Side-mounted crank could be attached at rear to main shaft, increasing the rate of fire
Rebounding firing pins introduced
Longer bolts to accommodate Accles feed
Improved extractors, i.e. wider
Internal parts made heavier
Safety added, permitted dry firing without firing pin damage, between trunnion and
    crank
Aiming bar and yoke unique to this model
Weight: 260 lbs.
Mounts: Steel and bronze Army standard; Watervliet Arsenal produced heavy wood
    carriages; Cone mounts standard for U.S. Navy, with some gunwale mounts and
    landing party carriages
STEAM GUN: U.S. Patent No. 311,973 of February 10, 1883

1885 MODEL 1885:
Improved ejector
Improved shell guide, to ensure ejection of fired cases

1886 MODEL 1886:
Similar to Model 1885

1887 MODEL 1887:
Similar to Model 1885

1889	**MODEL 1889:**

Improved Model 1881

10 x 32" .45-70 barrels, exposed

Either .45-70 Bruce or Gravity Feed

New style cocking switch, to permit dry firing, nicknamed the "Murphy Stop," which had to be both pulled out and rotated to disengage firing pins

Weight: 200 lbs.

Mounts: Steel, wooden wheels; steel handspike; Shields for gunner's protection introduced

1891	**MODEL 1891:**

Similar to Model 1889

1892	**MODEL 1892:**

Similar to Model 1889

Last .45-70 Gatlings purchased by the U.S. Army (18, Nos. 530-547)

1893	**MODEL 1893 Electric:**

10 x 32" barrels, bronze jacketed

Designed for naval service, driven by an electric motor powered by the vessel's generator

No provision for manual (crank) operation

Water cooled

MODEL 1893 Bulldog (Police):

6 x 12" .45-70 barrels, bronze jacketed

Accles feed

New wider extractors operated by cams instead of bolts

Weight: 74 lbs.

Mount: Low metal tripod standard

Note: Less than 10 reportedly manufactured, 10-barrel models offered

MODEL 1893:

First Gatlings chambered for .30-40

Introduced "Strip Feed," were altered to Bruce feed later (1897)

Bolts, breech casing, frame, main shaft and carrier block lengthened

Camming groove angles changed

Headspace adjustment altered, moved to cascabel knob, infinite settings

U.S. Army ordered 18 x 10" long barrel guns on June 19 at $1,100 each; had option to have Colt's alter to Bruce feed for $200 per gun

1895	**MODEL 1895:**

Improved version of Model 1893

Rebounding hammers added to bolts

Carrier block and hopper made of a special hard phosphor bronze

Bruce feed only

Gun port shield redesigned for improved protection and aiming

U.S. Army: 94 purchased, #1032–#1125

U.S. Navy: 1 purchased with an aluminum barrel jacket

6 x "short" 6mm Lee-Navy barrels

Accles drum feed

Metal tripod mounting

1897   Model 1893 Gatlings converted from strip feed to Bruce feed and headspace adjustment limited to 5 settings

1898   U.S. retired Accles feeds, replaced with Bruce feeds

U.S. Army received the following Model 1895 Gatlings fitted with Bruce feeds: May 20, 18 (#1032–#1049); August 29, 31 (#1050–#1080); November 28, 45 (#1081–#1125)

1900   **MODEL 1900:**

Minor variant of Model 1895

1897 headspace adjustment retained

Introduced marked settings for headspace adjustment: 0.051", 0.054", 0.057", 0.060", and 0.063"

Hopper machined from one piece of hard phosphor bronze

Model identification on right side of frame

Improved tolerance between barrels and bolts for improved interchangeability

Bruce feed

U.S. Navy: Bronze jacketed, as Model 1900 Mark II, Cal. .30

Crank could be side- or rear-mounted

Cocking switch (1883 type) retained

Sights on right side only, adjustable for elevation and windage

Both Colt's and U.S. Navy serial numbers

Estimated U.S. Navy purchase: 17

Mount: Lightweight landing party carriage or cone mount

1903   **MODEL 1903:**

Model 1900 chambered for .30-03

1906   **MODEL 1903–06:**

Conversion to .30-06 from .30-03. Last pattern manufactured by Colt's

34 altered by Colts, 1907, #1128–#1159, at $70 per gun

137 altered by Springfield Armory by 1909

"-06" added after serial number, e.g., 1155-06

New sights calibrated for .30-06 cartridge fitted

UNITED STATES GOVERNMENT PURCHASES OF GATLING GUNS

Model No.	Caliber	Serial Nos.	Year Delivered	Qty.	Purchasing Authority	Maker
1862	.58 Rimfire	unknown	1863	12	Maj. Gen. B. Butler	Cincinnati Type Foundry
	.58 Rimfire	unknown	1863	1	Adm. D.D. Porter	Cincinnati Type Foundry
1866	1"	unknown	1866	12	Maj. Gen. W.S. Hancock	Cooper F.A Mfg. Co.
1866	Improved .50-70	1–3, 5–8, 12–17, 19–26	1866	21	U.S. Navy	Colt's
		4, 9–11, 18, 34–44, 46–48, 50, 51, 53–55	1866	24	U.S. Army	Colt's
	1"	1–23, 26–35, 37–52	1866	49	U.S. Army	Colt's
1871	.50-70	100–108	1871	9	U.S. Army	Colt's
	.50-70	unknown	1871	unknown	U.S. Navy	Colt's
	1"	121	1871	1	U.S. Army	Colt's Last 1"
1874 Camel	.45-70	1–56	1874	56	U.S. Army	Colt's
1874 Long	.45-70	57–63, 105	1874	8	U.S. Army	Colt's
1875 Camel	.45-70	159–162	1875	4	U.S. Army	Colt's
1875 Long	.45-70	107–146, 163–166	1875	44	U.S. Army	Colt's
1875 Navy	.45-70	unknown	1875		unknown	U.S. Navy
1876 Long	.45-70	170–188	1876	19	U.S. Navy	Colt's
1877 Long	.45-70	191–193, 196–201 225, 226	1877	11	U.S. Army	Colt's Colt's #s used 2x
1877 Bulldog	.45-70	190, 203–218	1877	17	U.S. Army	Colt's
	.45-70	unknown	1877	unknown	U.S. Navy	Colt's
1879	.45-70	225, 226, 228, 229, 231–242	1879	18	U.S. Army	Colt's #s used 2x
1879	.45-70	245–258	1880	14	U.S. Army	Colt's
1881	.45-70	295–319	1881	25	U.S. Army	Colt's
1881	.45-70	321–323	1882	2	U.S. Army	Colt's
1883	.45-70	342–381	1883	40	U.S. Army	Colt's
1885	.45-70	405–425	1885	21	U.S. Army	Colt's
1886	.45-70	431–450	1886	20	U.S. Army	Colt's
1887	.45-70	457–476	1887	20	U.S. Army	Colt's
1889	.45-70	492–509	1889	18	U.S. Army	Colt's
1891	.45-70	510–527	1891	18	U.S. Army	Colt's
1892	.45-70	530–547	1892	18	U.S. Army	Colt's
1893	.30-40	1001–1018	1893	18	U.S. Army	Colt's
1895	.30-40	1032–125	1898	94	U.S. Army	Colt's
1900 Mark II	.30-40	unknown	1900	17?	U.S. Navy	Colt's
1900	.30-40	1126–1170	1900	45	U.S. Army	Colt's
1903	.30-03	1128–1159*	1903	32	U.S. Army	Colt's
1903–06	.30-06	unknown	1906–09	171	U.S. Army	Colt's

*Duplication of serial numbers is due to conversions to .30-06.
Only serial numbers 225 and 226 were used twice by the factory after 1874.

Springfield Armory Gatling Gun Related Operations
By Selected Fiscal and Calendar Years
1872–1917

1872:

Purchases and/or Manufactures:

9 Carriages, Gatling Gun

378 Feed Cases

Issues:

17 Gatlings, .50-70 and 1"

17 Carriages, .50-70 and 1"

15 Caissons, .50-70 and 1"

6,000 rounds 1" Ball ammunition

4,000 rounds 1" Canister ammunition

1873:

Purchases:

50 .45-70 Gatling Guns

2 "large caliber" Gatling Guns

Issues:

2 .50-70 Gatling Guns

1 1" Gatling Gun

3 Carriages, .50-70 and 1"

1 Caisson, Gatling Gun

15,000 rounds 1" Ball ammunition

10,000 rounds 1" Canister ammunition

1874:

Manufactures:

40 Arms Chests, Gatling Gun, with a cost of $3.50 each. Outside dimensions of these wooden boxes were: 4', 6³/₄" long x 1', 1³/₈" wide x 1', ¹/₂" deep.

Weight, empty: 57 lbs.

1875:

Manufactures:

1 Field Carriage, Gatling Gun at a cost of $250

1 Gauge, for Gatling Gun oscillator at a cost of $35

Published *Rules for the Inspection of Army Revolvers and Gatling Guns,* by Capt. J.P. Farley, Ordnance Department, on December 20th

1876:

Manufactures:

220 Manuals, Colt's Revolvers and Gatling Guns at a cost of 50 cents each

1877:

Manufactures:

40 Drifts (punches) for Gatling Guns, with a cost of 5 cents each

1878:

Purchases:

17 short (5) barrel .45-70 Gatlings

11 long (10) barrel .45-70 Gatlings

36 Carriages and Limbers, .45-70

53 Tripods, .45-70

2,145 Feed Cases (magazines), .45-70

Issues, Army:

3 .45-70 long Gatlings

10 .45-70 short Gatlings

2 .50-70 Gatlings

2 1" Gatlings

10 Carriages, for short Gatlings

7 Carriages and Limbers, for long Gatlings

2 Caissons and Limbers, Gatling

30 Gatling Covers

2 "extra gears"

5,000 rounds 1" Ball ammunition

2,000 rounds 1" Canister ammunition

18 Wheels, for Gatling carriages

4 Traces, for Gatling harnesses

Issues, Militia:

2 .50-70 Gatlings

15 .45-70 long (10) barrel Gatlings

16 Carriages and Limbers, for .45-70 Gatlings

2 Carriages and Limbers, for .50-70 Gatlings

670 Feed Cases, .45-70

8 Gun Covers, .45-70 long

1,000 rounds 1" Ball ammunition

1,000 rounds 1" Canister ammunition

1884:

A new all-metal carriage was designed and produced at Watervliet Arsenal. Interestingly, the name of the Accles feed was misspelled as "Eccles" in the official description of this carriage when it was published the following year.

1885:

Manual describing the "all-metal" Gatling Gun carriage published by Watervliet Arsenal, February 2. This is the manual with the "Eccles" typographical error.

1886:

Purchases:

25 .45-70 long (10) barrel Gatlings

100 Feed Cases, .45-70

80 Feed Magazines, .45-70

Manufactures:

20 Carriages and Limbers, .45-70

1 Limber, .45-70

38 Gun Covers

20 Mounts (Yokes?)

15 Sight Cases

24 Feed Guides

12 Feed Hoppers

Issues, Army:

1 short (5) barrel .45-70 Gatling

3 long (10) barrel .45-70 Gatlings

2 Cavalry Carts

2 Carriages and Limbers

Implements

6 Firing Pins

2 Oilers, for Carriage

Issues, Militia:

20 long (10) barrel .45-70 Gatlings

7 Carriages and Limbers, metal, .45-70

13 Carriages and Limbers, .45-70

Implements

NOTE: At the Cheyenne Ordnance Depot, Dept. of the Platte, the following were overhauled
and cleaned:

2 short .45-70 Gatlings

2 long .45-70 Gatlings

1890:

Purchases:

18 Model 1881 .45-70 Gatlings

Manufactures:

13 Gun Covers

10 Feed Guides

1 Feed Hopper

1 Sight Cover

Issues, Army:

1 long (10) barrel Gatling

4 short (5) barrel Gatlings

1 Cavalry Cart

3 Tripods

1 Carriage and Limber

Implements

1 Firing Pin

2 Firing Pin Springs

Issues, Militia:

10 long (10) barrel .45-70 Gatlings

7 Carriages and Limbers, metal, .45-70

3 Carriages and Limbers, .45-70

Implements

Issues, Colleges:

3 long (10) barrel .45-70 Gatlings

3 Carriages and Limbers, .45-70

8 Feed Magazines

2 Gun Covers

2 Oilers

Metallic Field Carriage adopted, as Model 1890

1891:

Purchases:

13 parts for Model 1883 Gatlings

1892:

Purchases:

82 parts for Model 1883 Gatlings

1893:

Tested a sample .30-40 Gatling with a "strip" feed

June 19: Ordered 18 .30-40 Gatlings (10 barrel) from Colt's, to be delivered by December. Each gun to have 200 strip feeds; Springfield Armory could manufacture without payment of royalties to Colt's.

Manufactures:

20 Carriages, metal, for .45-70 Gatlings

20 Limbers, for above

1 Pole, for Gatling Carriage

1 Saddle for Gatling Cavalry Cart

Issues:

3 long (10) barrel .45-70 Gatlings

1 Carriage without limber

2 Carriages and Limbers

1 Carriage, metal, for Gatling

1 Limber, for above

Appendages, .45-70

1 Axis pin, washer and nut

1 Binding Box, plate, screw, pin, washer and key [for aiming bar]

1 crank handle and pin

1 Pointing Lever (a.k.a. Aiming Bar)

1 Pole for Gatling Carriage

1 Saddle for Cavalry Cart harness

1894:

Above 18 Gatlings reported as delivered

The Property Return listed three models of Gatling Guns; Model 1881, Model 1883 and "10 barrels, long, caliber .50"

First "feed strip" complaints recorded

1895:

January 16: Contract with Gatling Gun Co. for 13 long barrel .30-40 guns, with Bruce feed

June 1893 contract guns to be altered for Bruce feed

January contract guns delivered by December 1

1896:

Model 1893s (18) being converted to Model 1895s

Model 1893/95 guns and a "number" of .45-70 guns assigned for fortification use, on metal carriage, Model 1890

Published manual on Model 1895 .30-40 Gatling Gun, on November 28

Cardboard 20-round .30-40 cartridge boxes redesigned for use with Bruce feeds

1897:

Model 1893s (18) converted to Model 1895s with Bruce feed, completed by June 30

Some 76 .45-70 in various models received for alteration to Bruce feed; work was underway

March 8: Contract for 31 Model 1895, .30-40 guns signed; inspection to be done by Springfield

September 9: Contract for 18 guns, .30-40

1898:

March 8, 1897, contract extended to permit delivery before September 20, 1898

61 Gatlings (.45-70) altered to Bruce feed

9 (.45-70) altered for gravity feed and fortress (casemate) mount

5 (.45-70) altered for casemate mount that were manufactured as Bruce feed

1899:

November 28: Contract for 45 long-barrel .30-40 Gatlings, Model 1900

Feed hopper wall redesigned to reduce jams

Bruce feed modified to let cartridge rim slide freely

Revised Property Return listed only two models of the Gatling Gun, i.e., Models 1881 and 1883.

The *Statement of Principal Serviceable Ordnance Stores For Issue* was revised on June 23, to include the following Gatling Guns: 10 barrels, long, .30-40 (Bruce feed); 10 barrels, long, .30-40 (positive feed); 5 barrel, short, .45-70; 10 barrels, short, .45-70; Model 1877 (10 barrel, long) .45-70; Model 1879 (10 barrels, long) .45-70; Model 1881 (10 barrels, long) .45-70; Model 1883 (10 barrels, long) .45-70. Accles feed; Model 1892 (10 barrels, long) .45-70, Bruce feed; No model, 10 barrels, long, .45-70 (Bruce feed); No model, 6 barrels, long, 1". This form was to be submitted on each January 31 by Frankford Arsenal, Columbia Arsenal, Benicia Arsenal and Augusta Arsenal.

1900:

Repairs:

10 Gatling Guns

1901:

2 Gatlings cleaned, repaired and altered

1903:

Inspected 10 Model 1901 (1900?) Navy pattern .30-40 Gatlings, with spare parts, etc., including:

10 Carriages and Limbers

10 Tripods

10 Mounts (presumed to be the yoke)

Published "revised" manual on .30 caliber Gatling Guns, Models of 1895 and 1900, on June 23

1904:

Gatlings under contract inspected at Colt's and delivered to Springfield Armory:

40 Model 1903 Gatlings, .30-03, with spare parts, etc. accepted

Manufactures:

41 Cleaning Rods

2 Gauges, special

26 Shell Drivers

1905:

Repairs:

3 Gatling Guns

1 Field Carriage and Limber

Manual published, June 1

1906:

4 Gatling sights altered to correspond to 2,200 fps muzzle velocity [.30-03 cartridge]

Revised manual published, October 15

1907:

Inspected 34 Model 1903 Gatlings converted by Colt's from .30-03 to .30-06 at a cost of $70.00 per gun. Serial Nos. 1128–1159. All subsequent conversions were by Springfield Armory to save money.

1908:

Lt. Crose prepared a revised manual for the Model 1895 and Model 1900 .30 caliber Gatlings. Assigned Manual No. 1757. 250 printed on June 23

1909:

Model 1903 Gatlings converted to .30-06. NOTE: The conversion process included Model 1895 and Model 1900 Gatlings originally manufactured for the .30-40 cartridge. A total of 171 Gatlings were altered to .30-06, including 40 new Model 1903s. Conversions had "-06" added to the serial number. In addition to new barrels, new sight leafs calibrated for the .30-06 cartridge were installed.

1910:

Lt. Meals prepared a new manual for .30 caliber Gatlings, April 11. 500 printed.

Covered .30-06 caliber Models of 1895, 1900 and 1903.

1911:

Last production of the Gatling Gun by Colt's.

28 Gatlings converted to .30-06, proofed, targeted at 500 and 1,000 yards

1912:

55 Gatlings proof fired and targeted. These were conversions to .30-06

1917:

New manual published for .30 caliber Gatlings, August 27. 500 printed.

NOTE: In addition to the conversion of Model 1895, Model 1900 and Model 1903 Gatlings to .30-06 during 1907–1909, the following Model 1866 .50-70 Gatlings were converted, after 1874 and prior to 1893, to fire the .45-70 cartridge: Serial Nos. 1, 2, 4–12, 14, 18–32, 34–44, 46–48, 50, 51, 53–55.

Total Conversions Recorded:

To .45-70-500	46
To .30-06	171

U.S. INSPECTORS OF GATLING GUNS

Initials	Name	Years Active
JCA	J.C. Ayers	1881–1883
OWA	O.W. Ainsworth	1831–1870
APC	A.P. Casey	1861–1886
DFC	David F. Clark	1861–1886
RAC	Rinaldo A. Carr	1889–1909
JEH	Maj. Jay E. Hoffer	1903–
KSM	Kelley S. Morse	1893–1915
HN	Henry Nettleton	1876–1880
FHS	Frank H. Schofield	1897–1901
	Lt., USN	Mark I

Note that the time span indicated is the period these inspectors worked; they also inspected arms other than Gatling Guns. Other inspectors marks may appear on U.S. issue Gatling Guns.

GATLING GUN INVENTORY • U.S. ARSENALS
November 17, 1875
.45-70 Ten-Barrel Model 1874 Gatlings

Arsenal:	Quantity:	To Be Issued To:
San Antonio	10	Department of Texas
Fort Union	5	Department of the Missouri
Rock Island	8	Department of Dakota
Rock Island	9	Department of the Platte

To be issued with a suitable supply of ammunition and harnesses for 2 horses, i.e., the U.S. Cavalry Cart pattern mount.

GATLING GUN INVENTORY
U.S. Army • 1895

Quantity	Caliber	Model and Description
50	.50-70	Model 1866, 6 barrel
9	.50-70	Model 1871, 6 barrel
50	1"	Model 1866, 6 barrel
1	1"	Model 1871, 10 barrel, serial no. 121
349	.45-70	Model 1874 and later, 10 barrel*
17	.45-70	Model 1877 Bulldog, 5 barrel
18	.30-40	Model 1893, 10 barrel

*May include the 46 .50-70 Gatlings altered to .45-70

U.S. ARMY ISSUES IN TEXAS
1875

Fort/Post: Guns:	1"	.50-70	.45-70
Fort Clark		2	
Fort Concho		2	1
Fort Davis	2		
Fort Duncan		1	
Fort Elliot	1		
Fort Griffin	2		
Fort McKavett		2	
Fort Quitman		2	
Fort Richardson	1		
Ringgold Barracks		1	
Fort Stockton	—	2	—
TOTALS:	6	12	1

U.S. NAVY GATLINGS
In The Spanish-American War
1898

As "Secondary Batteries" on board the:

First Class Steel Battleship:

U.S.S. *Maine*	4 Gatlings
U.S.S. *Missouri*	4 Gatlings
U.S.S. *Ohio*	4 Gatlings

Protected Steel Cruiser:

U.S.S. *San Francisco*	4 Gatlings

The balance of the capital ships in the fleet appear to have been armed with Colt Model 1895 Machine Guns, either two or four per vessel.

OTHER U.S. SALES/USAGE

1863: *The New York Times* reportedly purchased 3 during New York City draft riots.

1877: Philadelphia National Guard had at least 1.

1877: 23rd Regiment, New York Militia used one during July, at Hornellsville, in Erie Railroad Strike.

1877: On July 31, General Thomas Hillhouse, Assistant Treasurer, U.S. Department, New York City, requested arms be supplied to protect the depositary. Colonel Z.B. Tower, Corps of Engineers, specified the following: 2 Gatling Guns, 100 Rifles, 50 Revolvers plus Hand grenades. Issue was completed during October 1877.

1880: On December 7, the Secretary of the Treasury requested that the Secretary of War deliver the following arms for protection of the Sub-Treasuries: 3 Gatling Guns (.45-70), 1 Tripod for a .45-70 Gatling Gun, 300 cases of .45-70 Gatling Gun cartridges. Issue was made during December 1880.

1880s: Kansas State Guard had a Gatling Gun Battery, armed with Model 1879 Gatlings

1883: San Francisco, California, Police Department had 1.

1885: Connecticut Militia had two Machine Gun Platoons armed with Gatlings

1891: Issued by Tennessee National Guard

1892: Pennsylvania National Guard had "several."

1892: Hartford, Connecticut, Police Department, 1 Model 1893 Bulldog (Police).

1890s: Ohio Militia had Gatlings in service; crews were armed with Spencer shotguns.

1895: Company D, California Naval Reserve received their first Accles .30-40 Machine Gun, June 2.

1896: 1st Infantry of Illinois National Guard took up a "subscription" for 1 Gatling Gun.

1897: General Nelson A. Miles suggested mounting Gatling Guns on the rooftops of all U.S. Sub-Treasury buildings and Mints.

1898: The U.S. Navy had equipped the battleships *Maine, Missouri* and *Ohio* each with 4 Gatling Guns: the cruiser *San Francisco* also had 4.

1898: Employed during Spanish-American War, notably at Battle of San Juan Hill, Cuba

1902: 3rd Battery, New York National Guard replaced their Gatling Guns with 12 Model 1895 Colt Machine Guns.

1904: 2nd Regiment of Colorado National Guard used Model 1895 Gatling(s) during Cripple Creek miner's strike.

1907: Francis Bannerman, New York City military surplus dealer, mounted a surplus Gatling Gun on his "new power launch Polopel" and offered the armed vessel for sale for use in "Coast Guard Patrol" work. The price would be quoted on application.

SALES OF SURPLUS U.S. GATLINGS

As various models of U.S. Gatlings became obsolete, they were sold as surplus. The major purchaser was Francis Bannerman, of New York City. His catalogue of military goods was to be found in the offices of Ministers of War throughout the world. From 1902 onward, this catalogue included ex-United States Gatlings. Some sample listings follow:

1902:

6 each .50-70 Gatlings, long 6-barrel model, on field carriage (4' wheels), with feed cases, $600.00 each. Limbers were available at $90.00 each; Caissons were also for sale at $85.00 each.

1 each Carriage for a 1" Gatling, with trunnions and automatic traversing mechanism, $125.00

1 each .45-70 Gatling, short 6-barrel model, brass encased barrels (Naval model), traversing mechanism, on a steel Naval carriage, with full chest of feed cases, $750.00

1 each .50-70 Gatling, 10 long barrels, on Army field carriage, with limber and feed cases, automatic traversing mechanism. $750.00. No extra charge for this gun mounted on a Tripod

1 each 1" Gatling Gun Carriage, almost new, $150.00

1905:

1 each 1" Gatling Gun, 10 barrels on carriage, with feed cases, $2,500.00

4,000 1" Gatling Canister Cartridges, loaded with 15 lead balls, prices on application

4,000 1" Gatling Ball Cartridges, $25.00 per 100

10 each .50-70 Gatling Guns, on field carriages with attached ammunition chests, also feed cases, $750.00 each

Lot Gatling Gun Caissons, "offered with Gatling Guns and Limbers"

5 each 1" Gatling Guns, 6 barrels, with feed cases, $2,000.00 each

1 each .45-70 Gatling Gun, with Accles Drum, offered on an Army field howitzer carriage and limber, $1,200.00

Lot Accles Drums, for .45-70 cartridges, "offered only with the guns"

60,000 .45-70 Accles Feed Blank Cartridges, $16.50 per 1,000

6 each .30-40 Gatling Guns, Bruce Feed, on Army field carriages, New, with feeds, $2,000.00 each

Lot .45-70 Gatling Guns, 10 short barrels with brass jacket, U.S. Navy surplus, with Accles feeds, adapted to field carriages, with limbers, $1,200.00 each

1 each .30-40 Gatling Gun, 10 long barrels, mounted on a "shipboard" carriage, $2,000.00

10 each .45-70 Gatling Guns, mounted on field carriages, with limbers, feed cases, implements, covers, etc., $1,000.00 each

6 each .45-70 Gatling Guns, 10 barrel, with fixtures for mounting on launches or U.S. Navy field carriages, $1,000.00 each

Lot Gatling Gun Covers, prices on application

Lot Gatling Guns, mounted on Tripods, prices on application

Lot Gatling Gun Limbers, holding feed cases, "…will be furnished with Caliber .45 and .30 straight feed Gatlings if desired"

1 each Limber for 1" Gatling Gun, complete, $75.00

1 each .50-70 Gatling Gun, mounted on Cavalry Cart, $700.00

400,000 .50-70 Cartridges, loaded by U.S. Cartridge Company, for use in .50 caliber Gatling Guns, $16.50 per 1,000

1 each .50-70 Gatling Gun, mounted on "Special Naval Carriage," $900.00

GATLING GUN MAKERS

U.S.A.:

Miles H. Greenwood Foundry & Machine Works, Cincinnati, OH: 1862	Manuf. 6
Cincinnati Type Foundry Works, Cincinnati, OH: 1863	Manuf. 13
Cooper Fire Arms Mfg. Co., Philadelphia, PA: 1865–1866	Manuf. 8 1"
Colt's Pat. F.A. Mfg. Co., Hartford, CT: 1866 until 1911	Manuf. 1,265+

Austria:

Ed. A. Paget & Co. — Vienna, before 1869, on verge of bankruptcy in 1871
> Reported to have made "sub-standard" quality Gatlings; involvement with the Hotch-kiss Revolving 37mm Cannon contributed to ending relations with The Gatling Gun Co.

China:

Nanking Arsenal: 1874–1888, made both low wheeled field carriages and tripods as mounts for the "Gatlings" they produced.

Russia:

Nobel Brothers, Petersberg

Russian armories, rights granted, without royalty payments, on November 16, 1869

Production began during 1870, 400 made, known as "Gorloffs" after the Russian inspector assigned to Colt's, Colonel A. Gorloff (promoted to Major General in 1870)

United Kingdom:

Sir William Armstrong & Co., Newcastle-on-Tyne, England

Manufacturing agreement signed 1869 or 1870, renewed in 1881

1870: Armstrong to produce 200 Gatlings at £103 each

1873: Armstrong to be paid an additional 5% commission on sales price

1875: Armstrong to be paid £113 for each rifle caliber Gatling and £150 for each .65 caliber gun. An additional 5% was paid for retooling costs and 5% commission on any orders generated by Armstrong

Sales Prices: £205 for rifle caliber guns, £265 for .65 caliber guns

1887: Displayed a Gatling at the Queen Victoria's Jubilee International Exposition held at Newcastle

The Gatling Gun Ltd., Perry Bar, near Birmingham, England, see details below

NOTE: All foreign-made Gatling Guns in rifle (musket) calibers were of the 10-barrel pattern; 1" guns were made in both 6- and 10-barrel patterns.

The Gatling Gun, Ltd.

The Gatling Gun Ltd. was incorporated in the United Kingdom on April 4, 1888, as a European subsidiary of the Gatling Gun Company. It was sold on April 20, 1888, to William C. Penfield, of London for $50,000 together with all European patent rights for an additional $100,000. The patents purchased by The Gatling Gun, Ltd. included:

English Patents

Battery Gun	No. 790/1865 (March 21)
Improvement to Battery Gun	No. 3,341/1869 (Nov. 19)
Battery Gun	No. 2,954/1871 (Nov. 3)
Cartridge Feeder for Machine Guns	No. 4,211/1881 (Sept. 29)
Machine Gun and Feeder	No. 5,436/1881 (Dec. 13)
Cartridge Charger for Machine Gun Feeders	No. 6,009/1886 (May 4)
Cartridge Feeder for Machine Guns	No. 7,659/1886 (June 8)

French Patents

Machine Gun and Feeder	No. 147,224
Upright Feed for Machine Guns	No. 175,909

Italian Patents

Machine Gun and Feeder	No. 15,682
Upright Feed for Machine Guns	No. 20,049

Belgian Patents

Machine Gun and Feeder	No. 56,986
Upright Feed for Machine Guns	No. 73,398

Austro-Hungarian Patent

Machine Gun and Feeder	No. 27,250

The Gatling Arms & Ammunition Co., Ltd. was established in Birmingham, England, in 1888. It was the immediate successor company to The Gatling Gun Limited, and was incorporated for £800,000 but only raised £371,270. On February 4, 1890, a petition for voluntary liquidation was filed. This order was granted in September 1891. In January 1891, the Gatling Gun Company was awarded a judgement against this company. No additional information on the case has been found, but it is suspected that either the 1889 Danish contract to rebuild several .42 Berdan Gatlings to 8mm Danish, or the sale of eight Gatlings (without payment of royalties) to the Chilean Navy that same year was the cause. The court-appointed liquidator was not released until 1895.

The next successor company was Grenfell & Accles Ltd., with James G. Accles a partner. They manufactured the Accles-improved Gatling at Holford Works, Parry Barr, Birmingham, England. This was the old National Arms & Ammunition Co., Ltd. plant. The Grenfell & Accles firm lasted from 1891 to 1896. These "improved" Accles guns were manufactured in the United States by the Driggs Ordnance Company of Washington, D.C.

Accles was also involved with two other British companies, The Accles Company and Accles & Shelvoke Company. They were successors to William Gardner's "machine gun" business (Gatling competitor) about the turn of the century.

OFFICERS AND OWNERS OF THE GATLING GUN COMPANY
Hartford, Connecticut
Incorporated in Connecticut, 1874

Original Incorporators:
Richard J. Gatling
James Goodwin
Henry Keney
Edgar T. Welles

Owners:
1874
R.J. Gatling referred to "McClure and Jones" as "major stockholders" in a letter to Edgar T. Welles

As of April 27, 1888:
Daniel Baird Wesson (of Smith & Wesson)	6%
Richard Jordan Gatling	10%
Colt's Patent Fire Arms Mfg. Co.	84%?

Chairman:
1875: John Love

Presidents:
1874–1896: Richard Jordan Gatling
1897–1902: John H. Hall
(also president of Colt's, 1901–1902)
1902–1909: Lewis C. Grover
(also president of Colt's)

Vice Presidents:
1874–   : George C. Summner
1897–1902: Lewis C. Grover

Secretary:
1873–1877: Edgar T. Welles
1877?–1900: Col. Frederick W. Prince

THE INDIANA-BASED GATLING GUN COMPANY, 1865–1874
24¹/₂ East Washington Street, Indianapolis

President: 1869–1871: W.H. Talbott

THE GATLING GUN COMPANY
1905–1906

The first *Thomas' Register of American Manufacturers* was published during 1905. This was a listing of manufacturers "and First Hands in All Lines." The companies were listed by category of product and location.

The following is the listing for the Gatling Gun Company:

CONN. — Hartford
Gatling Gun Co. (Gatling Guns) . . X

The "X" following this listing indicated that the company had supplied no financial information to the publisher; no capital rating had been established. The parent company, listed as "Colt's Arms Co." had a capital rating of "AAAA," the best available, indicating assets in excess of $1,000,000.00.

The signature of Richard Jordan Gatling
September 12, 1818–February 26, 1903

FOREIGN SALES/USAGE

Argentina:

"Several" before 1891 in 11mm Spanish

1 x 10-barrel 1" Model 1866, on locally made carriage to provide quick traversing and elevation

1 x .10 barrel .75 caliber Model 1866, on an improved version of the above carriage

Austria:

July 17, 1868: Tested at Vienna, .50-70, 10-barrel Gatling Gun

July 9, 1869: Trial at Vienna, .50-70 and .42 Berdan, 10-barrel Gatlings

1870–1873: Reported as "introduced in the service"

Late 1883: Trial of a Model 1883

Baden:

August 1869: Trial at Karlsruhe, .50-70, 10-barrel Gatling

Bavaria:

1867/8: Tested

Bolivia:

By 1879, 11mm Spanish

Canada:

April and May 1885: 2 used in Riel Rebellion, under command of an American, Lt. Arthur L. Howard, Connecticut National Guard

Chile:

By 1879, 11mm Spanish

1889: Purchased at least 8 for Navy from Gatling Gun Ltd., U.K., which at that time was not an affiliate of the American Gatling Gun Company.

China:

Purchased 10-barrel Model 1877 Bulldog Gatlings

Manufactured at Nanking Arsenal, 10-barrel pattern, during 1883

First 4 were completed by August 24, 1874, but first 2 needed some "tuning"

Production ceased in 1888 to produce "Maxim" machine guns

.45 "English" Gatling, locally loaded ctgs.

1" locally loaded ctgs.

Denmark:

October 14, 1867: Tested a 1" x 6-barrel Gatling, at Amager Common, near Copenhagen

Spring 1868: Trial of a "newer" 1" Colt's 6-barrel Gatling, Serial No. 2, on a Broadwell carriage, made in Karlsruhe, Germany

1868: Ordered an 11.45mm 10-barrel Gatling from Colt's

1869: Artillery ordered 3 x 1" Gatlings from Colt's, with carriages from Broadwell's factory in Karlsruhe.

1870: Extended trials of 1" Gatlings near Copenhagen

Spring/Summer 1871: Trials of 1" Gatling repeated with improved bullet alloy

October 17, 1870: Testing of the 11.45mm Gatling began

July 3, 1871: 2 Broadwell drums received from Ed. Paget & Co., in Vienna

July 1871: New sheet-metal carriage made, to replace the adapted artillery field carriage

November 1871: 2 x .42 Berdan 10-barrel Gatlings "borrowed" from the Gatling Gun Co. for testing. American ammunition supplied for this test. Had the 400-round Broadwell drum

December 1871 and January 1872: Test done with the .42 Berdan Gatlings

March 22, 1873: Continued testing of .42 Berdan Gatlings

September 19, 1873: Testing Commission recommended adoption of the Palmcrantz, invented in Sweden

1889: Gatlings with side-mounted Accles feeds mounted in new forts at Copenhagen, 8mm Danish, 10-jacketed barrels, as Model 1889. These were converted .42 Berdan Gatlings, the work being done by the Gatling Arms & Ammunition Co., Ltd. in Birmingham, England. They were mounted on metal tripods. This conversion may have led to the suit and judgement by the Gatling Gun Company in January 1891.

Egypt:

Adopted by 1882, 11mm Egyptian

France:

1867: 1" and .50-70 Improved Model 1866 demonstrated to Napoleon III

1868: 2 x "large" caliber 10-barrel guns delivered to Ministry of Marine (Navy) ca.1870: 1", 6-barrel

1870: 9 x .50-70, ex-U.S. Navy Gatlings purchased through Remington

Unknown: 1 x 6-barrel rifle caliber, 1 x 10-barrel rifle caliber

August/September 1877: Trials held at Bourge by the Artillery Commission

Guatemala:

At least 3, 11mm Spanish

Holland:

1867/8: Tested

Model 1871 Gatlings purchased, 11mm Beaumont

Italy:

October 10, 1883: Trials at Turin with a 10-barrel .45-70 Model 1883 Gatling and a 6-barrel .42 Berdan Gatling. The guns were fired at ranges of 500, 800, 1,000 and 1,800 meters for accuracy and speed. The .45-70 Gatling fired 800 rpm. In the accuracy tests, the Gatlings won.

Japan:

"Several" or "few," depending on report

Korea:

June 1891: 3 x .43 caliber Gatlings purchased; inspected/test fired by the U.S. Ordnance Department at Sandy Hook, NJ, on behalf of the Korean government.

Mexico:

At least 3, 11mm Spanish, purchased under Porfirio Diaz, by 1895, and before 1910. Included a Model 1877 Bulldog, mounted on a locally designed and manufactured "all-metal" field carriage.

Montenegro:

1895: 6 x Gatling-Gorloffs, .42 Berdan, a gift of the Russian Tsar

Morocco:

1888: Use reported, 11mm Egyptian?

Peru:

By 1879, 11mm Spanish

Prussia:

October 9, 1867: 1 x 1" , 6-barrel

1 x .50-70, 6-barrel

1 x .50-70, 10-barrel

This trial gun order included the rights to order up to 100 Gatlings

Rumania:

1875: Sample Gatling delivered to Bucharest; Broadwell expected an order for 12 or 18 Gatlings to result from trials.

Russia:

1865: 2 x Model 1862

1868: 20 x .42 Berdan, 10-barrel, delivery in 1869 @ U.S. $1,500 each May 13, 1869: 100 x .42 Berdan, 10-barrel Model 1871 Gatlings reported as purchased

Plus local production as "Gorloffs"

By 1876, some 400 "Gorloff's" produced by the Tsar's armories

Spain:

ca.1871: 11 x 57mmR (11mm Spanish)

December, 1876: 46 x Camel Guns, 11mm @ $920, w/tripods @ $80, traversing gear @ $40, packing @ $20 Presumed to be Model 1875; delivered to Cuba. Also reported as 50 guns

Sweden:

1867/68: Trials, lost to Palmcrantz by 1877

Switzerland:

1868: 1" x 6-barrel Gatling(s) in service

Tunis:

1875: 2 Model 1871 Gatlings purchased, 11mm Egyptian?

Turkey:

July 1870: 100 x .58 Turkish Snider, 10-barrel @ U.S. $950 without carriages or feeds

August 1870: 30 x .58 Turkish Snider, 10-barrel, for Navy

Note: Also reported as 200 for the Army; contract assigned to Paget in Vienna

United Kingdom:

March 7, 1867: Tested a 6-barrel 1" Gatling at Shoeburyness

August and September 1870: Shoeburyness trials of .42, .65 and 1"

1871: Adopted in .450/.577 with Broadwell drum

January 1872: .450 and .65 Gatlings ordered from W.G. Armstrong & Co.

January 1874: First guns from 1872 contract delivered.

1874: .45 cal. adopted, Mark I

December 1875: A total of 40 Gatlings delivered; 28 issued to the Royal Navy and 12 kept at Woolwich Arsenal. These were later delivered to the Royal Navy.

March 1878: At least 50 Gatlings in service with the Royal Navy

September 1879: Trials at Shoeburyness of a 6-barrel Gatling made by Armstrong

March 1881: War Office trials of the following .450 Gatlings:

    6-barrel, side crank

    10-barrel, rear crank

    10-barrel, side crank

1883: Gatlings requested for service in the West Indies; none were in storage

1884: Request for West Indies service repeated; none available

    A "quantity" reported ordered for the Royal Navy

1886: .65 caliber Gatlings purchased for Royal Navy

    October 1886: A .450 Gatling was delivered to the School of Musketry at Hythe

NOTE: There were four .450 caliber chamberings for the British Gatlings, the .450/.577 as used in the Martini-Henry Rifles and Carbines, the .450 Gatling, restricted to Gatlings, and the .450 Machine Gun. The first and last cartridges were loaded later (August 1903 and January 1895, respectively) with cordite. The .450 Gatling round was adopted during August 1874. It was primarily a navy round. The .450 Machine Gun cartridge was adopted in January 1883. A .450 Light Gatling round (also known as the .450 Mountain Gun) was adopted for service in India on February 1, 1879. Its case was slightly shorter than the standard load and used a lighter bullet. In addition to the standard lead bullets, examples with jacketed bullets are known. A blank load with a paper bullet was also produced after May of 1888. Dummies, proof rounds and armorer's dummies were also manufactured for these British Gatling Guns. All British calibers were loaded by Kynoch, among others.

RICHARD JORDAN GATLING'S
UNITED STATES PATENTS

May 10, 1844	Seed Planter	No.	3,581
April 14, 1847	Hemp Brake	No.	5,073
August 10, 1848	Seed Sowing Machine	No.	5,702
May 29, 1860	Rotary Plow	No.	28,465
July 3, 1860	Cultivator for Cotton Plants	No.	28,978
July 10, 1860	Lath Making Machine	No.	29,072
September 4, 1860	Improved Hemp Brake	No.	29,875
September 18, 1860	Gearing Machine	No.	30,059
September 9, 1862	Steam Driven Marine Ram	No.	36,402
November 4, 1862	Revolving Battery Gun	No.	36,386
May 9, 1865	Improved Battery Gun	No.	47,631
June 16, 1868	Priming Metallic Cartridges	No.	78,953
May 3, 1870	Improvement in Metallic Cartridges	No.	102,675
February 28, 1871	Revolving Battery Gun	No.	112,138
April 9, 1872	Improved Revolving Battery Gun	No.	125,563
December 16, 1873	Traversing Mechanism for Machine Guns	No.	145,563
February 10, 1885	Breechloading Ordnance	No.	311,973
February 10, 1885	Loading Device for Breechloading Guns	No.	311,974
April 10, 1888	Apparatus for Casting Ordnance	No.	380,756
March 12, 1889	Combined Torpedo and Gun Boat	No.	399,516
March 11, 1890	Mold Core for Patent No. 380,756	No.	423,045
March 25, 1890	Torpedo and Gun Boat	No.	424,288
May 13, 1890	Pneumatic Gun and Torpedo Boat	No.	427,847
May 13, 1890	Pneumatic Gun and Operating Mechanism	No.	427,848
August 19, 1890	Pneumatic Gun Valve	No.	434,662
June 9, 1891	Art of Making Ordnance	No.	453,833
March 1, 1892	Apparatus for Cleansing Wool or Other Material by the Use of Steam or Other Fluid	No.	469,822
May 9, 1893	Machine for Forging and Compacting Ingots	No.	496,873
May 23, 1893	Machine Gun	No.	497,781

May 8, 1894	Bicycle	No. 519,384
June 13, 1893	Machine Gun Feed	No. 499,534
July 25, 1893	Machine Gun	No. 502,185
August 8, 1893	Machine Gun Feed	No. 502,882
September 12, 1893	Machine Gun	No. 504,831
November 5, 1895	A Torch	No. 549,122
April 21, 1896	Combined Cotton Thinner and Cultivator	No. 558,682
October 10, 1899	Rein Controlling Means	No. 634,451
April 10, 1900	Machine for Thinning and Cultivating Cotton	No. 646,977
June 12, 1900	Cultivator	No. 651,659
October 23, 1900	Motor Driven Vehicle	No. 660,098
February 26, 1901	Flushing Apparatus for Water Closets	No. 668,853
April 1, 1902	Steam Powered Plow	No. 696,808
July 22, 1902	Motor Plow	No. 705,337

GATLING GUN RELATED
UNITED STATES PATENTS

James G. Accles

December 18, 1883	Machine Gun Feed Device	No. 290,622
August 31, 1886	Machine Gun Carriage	No. 348,180
January 22, 1889	Cartridge Feed Case	No. 396,523
April 22, 1890	Machine Gun	No. 426,356
December 6, 1892	Machine Gun Feed Device	No. 487,238

Lewis Wells Broadwell

December 20, 1870	Cartridge Feeder for Repeating Arms	No. 110,338

Clement M. Broderick and John Vankeirsbilck

September 5, 1893	Machine Gun Feed	No. 504,516
September 5, 1893	Machine Gun	No. 504,517

Lucien F. Bruce

September 20, 1881	Machine Gun Feed Device	No. 247,158
March 6, 1883	Cartridge Charger for Machine Gun Feeds	No. 273,249
May 4, 1886	Machine Gun Feed Device Loader	No. 341,371
June 8, 1886	Cartridge Charger for Machine Gun Feeds	No. 343,532
November 2, 1886	Cartridge Feeder for Machine Guns	No. 351,960

Carl J. Ehbetts

November 26, 1895	Gas Operated Machine Gun	No. 550,262

FOREIGN PATENTS

For a listing of foreign Gatling Gun patents, as of April 20, 1888, please refer to the section on THE GATLING GUN, LTD. on pages 22 and 23.

United States Patent No. 36,386
November 4, 1862

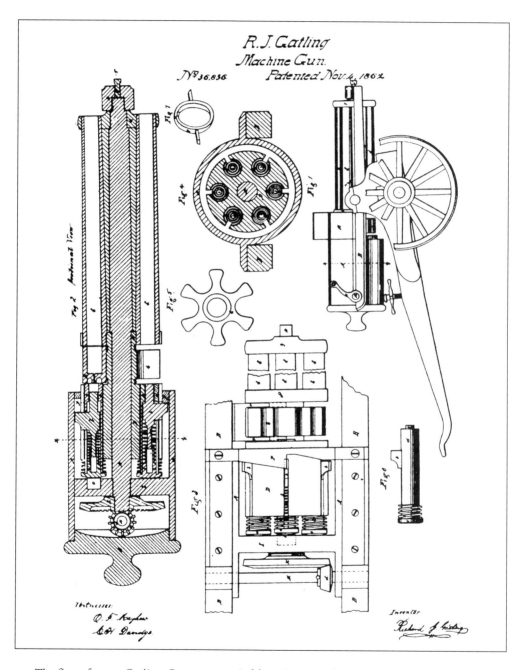

The first of many Gatling Gun patents. A 6-barrel .58 Musket Gatling Gun is shown in the drawings. This gun, using steel carriers for the paper .58 Musket cartridges, fired 200 rounds per minute. This was the only Gatling Gun not designed for metallic cartridges.

United States Patent No. 47,631
May 9, 1865

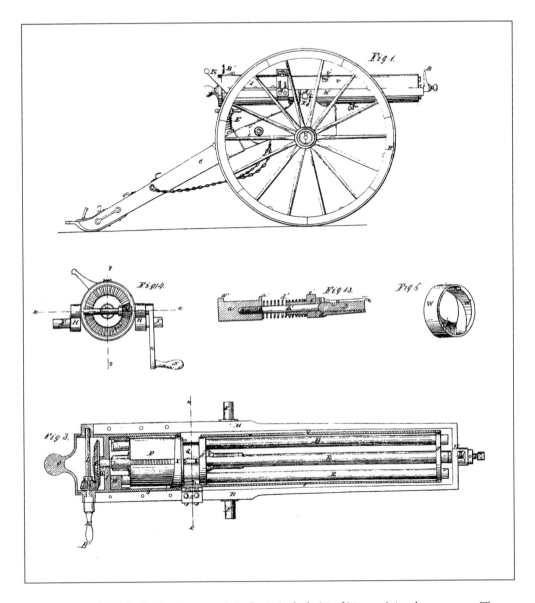

During 1865, R.J. Gatling improved the basic lock (bolt) of his revolving battery gun. These improvements were patented while he was a resident of Indianapolis, Indiana.

The breech mounted drive gears are shown in Figure 14. Figure 13 depicts the bolt and its wide firing pin for use with the .58 caliber rimfire cartridge. The cam that operated the bolts is shown in Figure 5. The spiral ramp provided the back-and-forth motion to the bolts as the barrels were rotated by the crank. Figure 3 is a drawing of the Gatling Gun mechanism without the breech housing in place.

United States Patent No. 110,338
December 20, 1870

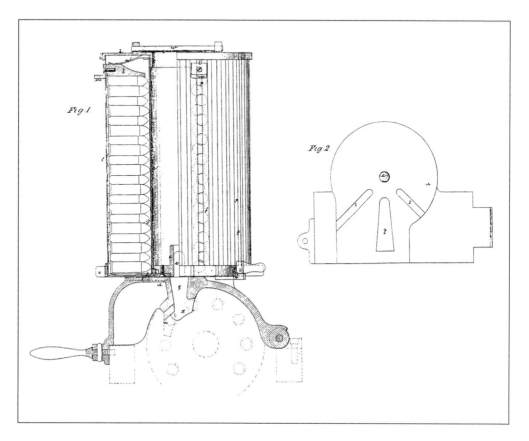

Lewis W. Broadwell developed and patented the first large-capacity feed device for Gatling Guns while a resident of Karlsruhe, Baden, Germany. The Broadwell Drum was adopted by the United States and the United Kingdom, to name but two countries using it.

In effect, the Broadwell Drum was a series of single-column magazines mounted about a central axis. As each column was emptied, the drum was rotated and a new column was then ready to feed the Gatling Gun.

This top-mounted magazine required the Gatling Gun to be fitted with a special feed plate (Fig. 2). Simpler forms of magazines replaced the Broadwell Drum.

United States Patent No. 112,138
February 28, 1871

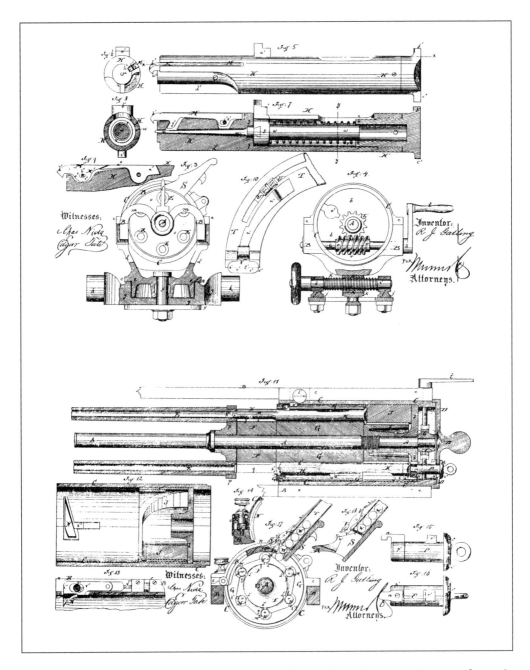

The improved revolving battery gun patented by R.J. Gatling. This gun, when manufactured by Colt's, introduced the curved magazine, heavier bolts and the access port in the breech housing. A rotating plug closed this port when the Gatling Gun was in use.

United State Patent No. 125,563
April 9, 1872

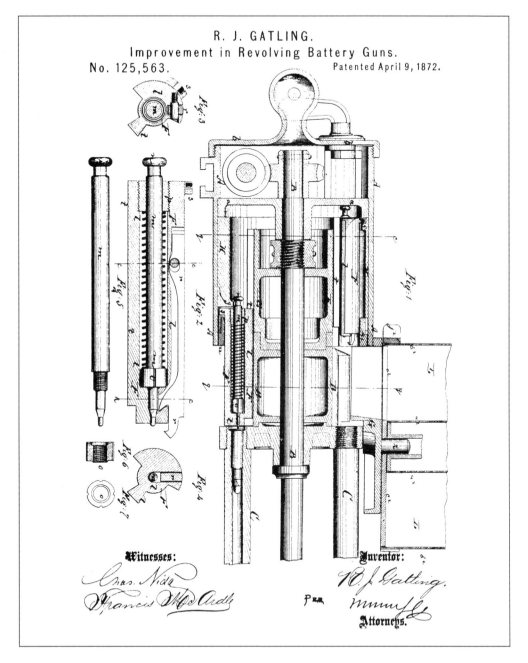

R. J. Gatling.'s improvements to his earlier designs included shorter bolts with guide ribs. The short bolt was not used in a production model Gatling until 1874. The magazine in this drawing is the Broadwell drum, introduced with the Model 1871 Gatling Gun.

United States Patent No. 145,563
December 16, 1873

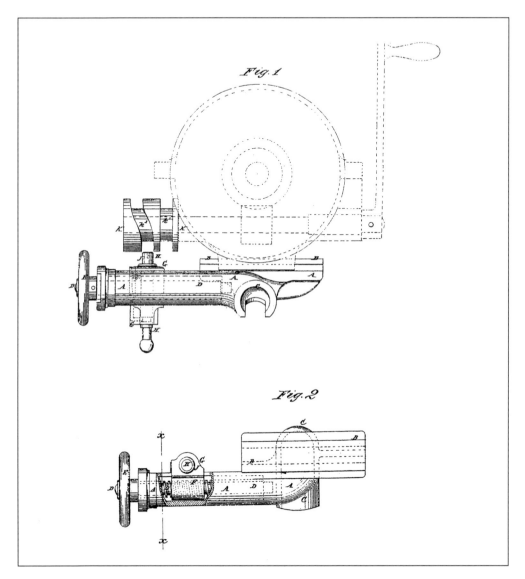

This patent was granted to R.J. Gatling for his improved traversing mechanism for the Gatling Gun. The device enabled the Gatling Gun to spread the bullets over a wide area without repositioning the artillery style carriage.

A cam (A) with two grooves was fitted to the left end of the crank shaft. A projection rode in the helical groove, causing the Gatling Gun to automatically move in a horizontal plane as it was fired. The width of the traverse was controlled by positioning the projection by means of a small hand-wheel (D). When the projection was placed in the non-helical groove, the Gatling did not traverse.

This feature was abandoned when the aiming or "pointing" bar was developed.

United States Patent No. 247,158
September 20, 1881

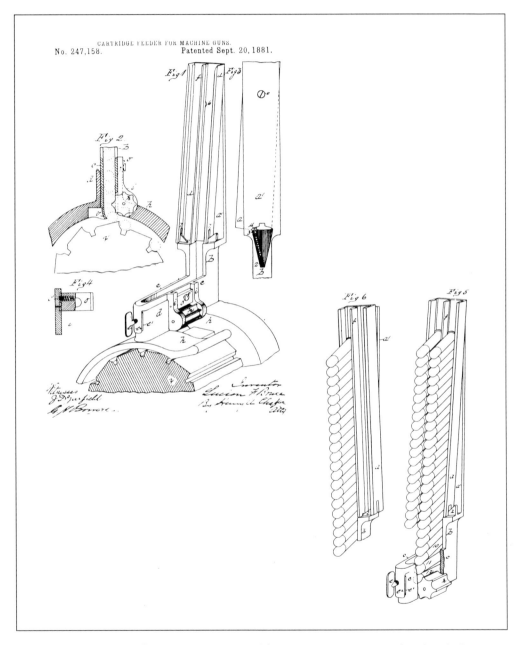

This double-column feed device was patented by L.F. Bruce. It was introduced with the Model 1881 Gatling Gun. Those Bruce Feeds manufactured by Colt's have the patent information on the back. Unmarked examples are those made at Springfield Armory. All U.S. Army "strip feed" Gatling Guns (e.g., Model 1893) were altered to the Bruce feed.

United States Patent No. 273,249
March 6, 1883

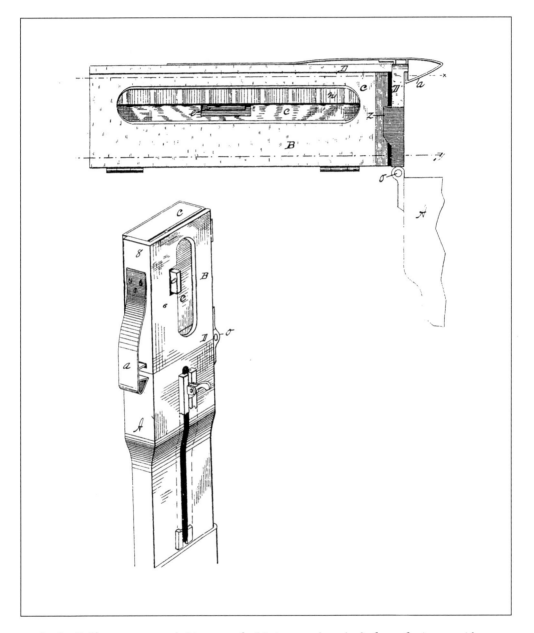

Lucien F. Bruce was granted this patent for his improved method of transferring cartridges from the cardboard boxes of 20 rounds to the gravity feed for the Gatling Gun.

A fitting on the top of the gravity feed magazine was opened, and two columns of cartridges were emptied into this fitting from the cardboard box. When the fitting was closed, the "cartridge feeder" transferred them into the single column required by the gravity feed magazine.

United States Patent No. 290,622
December 18, 1883

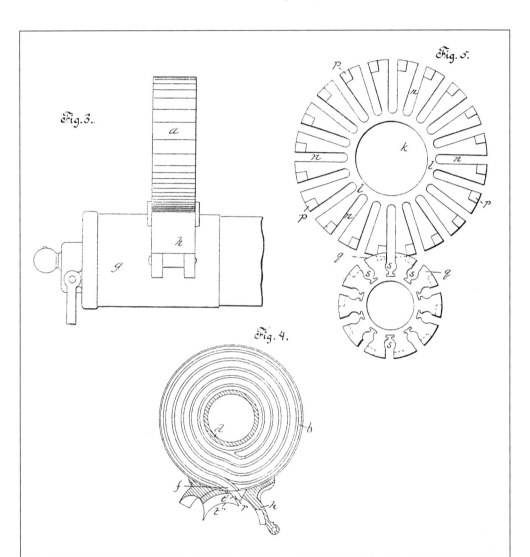

James G. Accles received this patent for what would become the Accles Drum. The patent was assigned to the Gatling Gun Company.

The cartridges were driven through a spiral groove (Fig. 4) inside the drum by a "propeller" (Fig. 5) and into the rotary feed block of the Gatling Gun. They were chambered by the bolts from this feed block.

The ammunition drum was filled (slowly) through the port in the base of the drum. A positive feed was claimed for both high and low elevations of the Gatling Gun.

This basic concept was applied to the drum magazines for the Thompson Submachine Gun, but improved by the addition of a removable cover to speed the filling process.

United States Patent No. 341,371
May 4, 1886

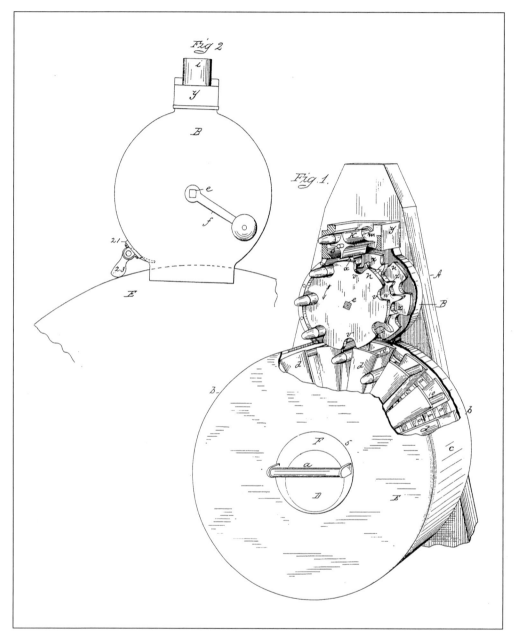

Lucian F. Bruce patented this loading device for the Accles Drum on May 4, 1886, some two and a half years after the drum itself was patented. The patent was assigned to the Gatling Gun Company, as was that for the Accles magazine. Bruce intended to increase the speed of filling the drum magazine.

United States Patent No. 343,532
June 8, 1886

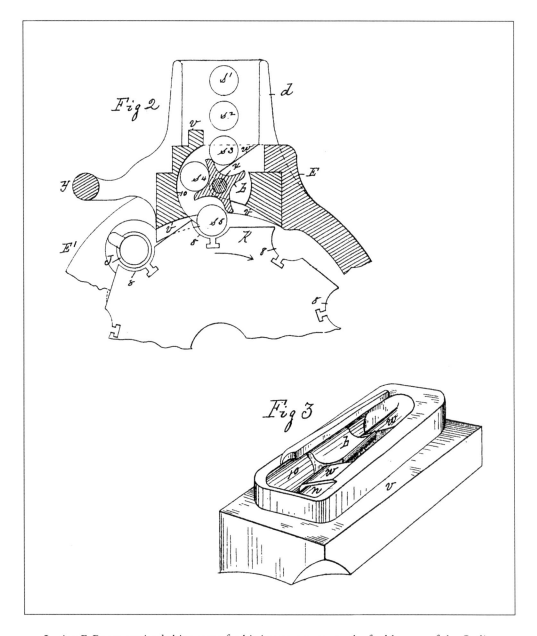

Lucien F. Bruce received this patent for his improvements to the feed hopper of the Gatling Gun. The newly designed feed hopper was used with the Bruce Feed patented during 1881.

The most important feature was a "fluted roller" (b) with its axis directly below the center line of the cartridges (S.1-S.5) in the Bruce Feed. This roller ensured that each round was properly aligned for chambering by the bolt in the uppermost barrel of the Gatling Gun.

United States Patent No. 348,180
August 31, 1886

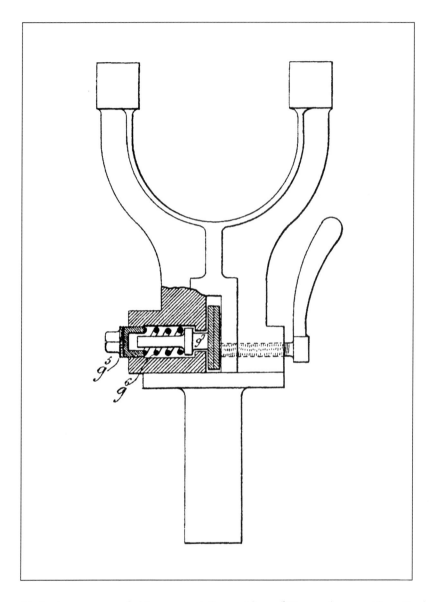

James G. Accles was granted this patent while a resident of Newcastle-upon-Tyne, England. The carriage was designed for "a machine-gun of the well-known Gatling type."

This new carriage design was intended to be more maneuverable; a pair of "pushing poles" were fitted to the carriage instead of the more traditional artillery-style handspike.

Perhaps the most important feature was a spring-loaded dog that acted to bind the elevation arc in the desired position. This was fitted to the base of the yoke that held the Gatling Gun in place on the Accles carriage.

United States Patent No. 351,960
November 2, 1886

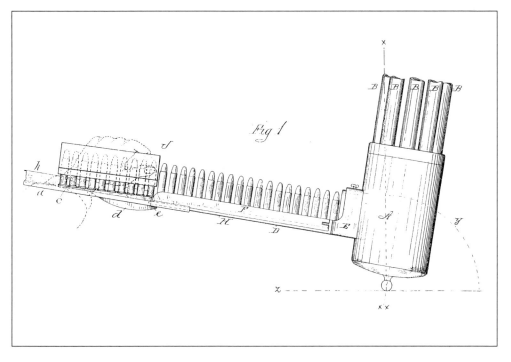

This patent, granted to Lucien F. Bruce, is an improvement to his 1881 patent for what became the Bruce Feed. The specifications indicate that this concept was to enable the feed to be filled while the Gatling Gun was elevated at a high angle.

A hinged plate (d) was attached to the usual Bruce Feed; when the Gatling Gun was elevated at a high angle, this plate was raised and acted as an extension of the Bruce Feed. The lip on the plate prevented the cartridges from spilling from the cardboard box of 20 when the box was inverted to fill the feed device.

This patent was assigned by Bruce to the Gatling Gun Company.

United States Patent No. 396,532
January 22, 1889

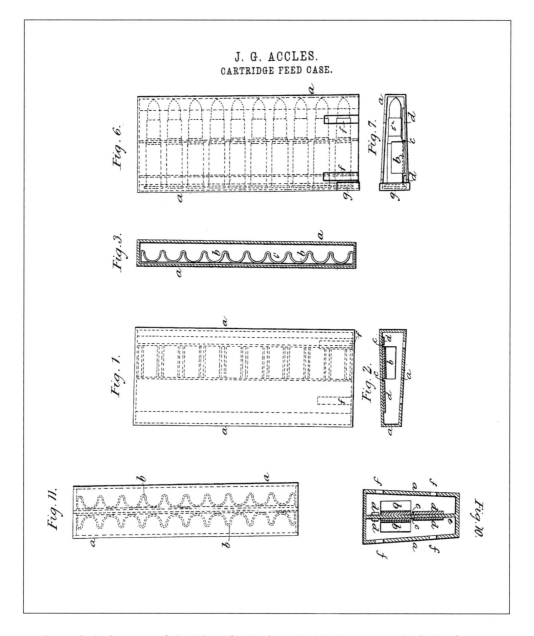

James G. Accles patented this "Cartridge Feed Case" while living in England. This box became an integral part of the machine gun's feed device, delivering single rounds to the feed mechanism of the Gatling Gun. It was designed to hold either 10 or 20 rounds. Almost four years later, Accles patented a feed mechanism to strip the ammunition from this box. These were the papier-mâché boxes that the United States government objected to.

United States Patent No. 426,356
April 22, 1890

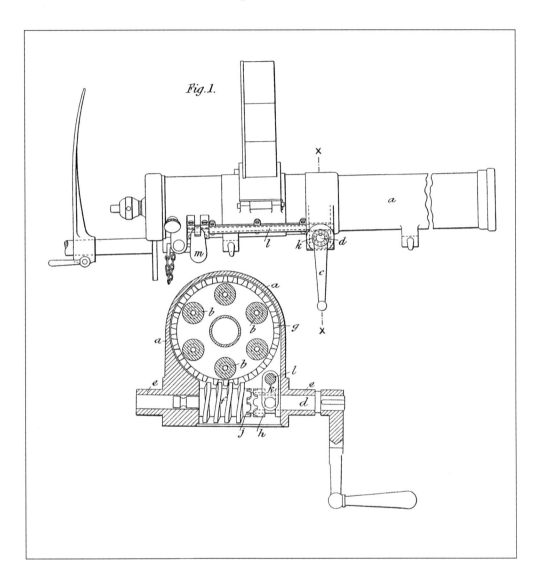

Fig.1.

James G. Accles was granted this patent while living in London, England. This improvement to the Gatling Gun was also patented by Accles in the United Kingdom (1888), France (1889), Belgium (1889) and Austria-Hungary (1889).

Accles moved the crank (c) from the breech housing to the right-hand trunnion (d). The drive to rotate the barrels and fire the gun was a worm gear. Pulling the crank to the right disengaged it from the drive train. This reduced the number of parts required and, in theory, improved the accuracy of the gun.

The Accles Gun illustrated above is fitted with the drum magazine he patented in 1883. Guns of this pattern were sold to the United States Navy and to Denmark.

United States Patent No. 487,238
December 6, 1892

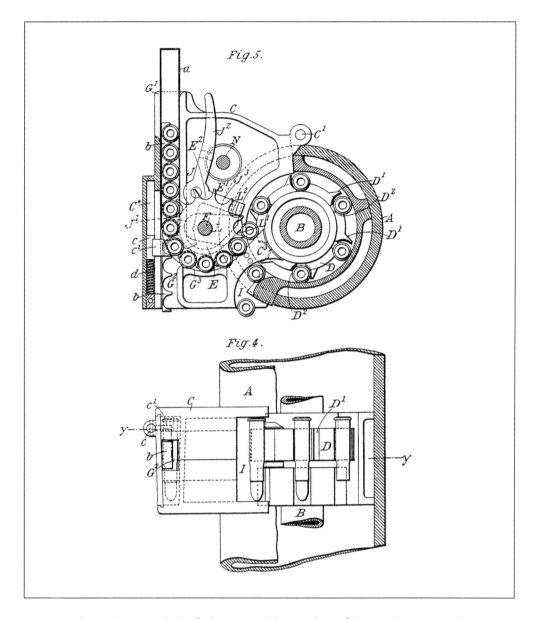

James G. Accles patented this feed system while a resident of Birmingham, England. He described it as being suitable for use with either a Gatling Gun or an Accles Gun.

This feed device was intended to replace his Accles Drum, patented in 1883. It used cartridge "packages" that Accles patented in 1889. They were placed in the feed hopper, and as the gun was fired, emptied of the cartridges, and then forced out, empty.

When applied to an Accles Gun, the system was rejected by the United States Navy.

United States Patent No. 497,781
May 23, 1893

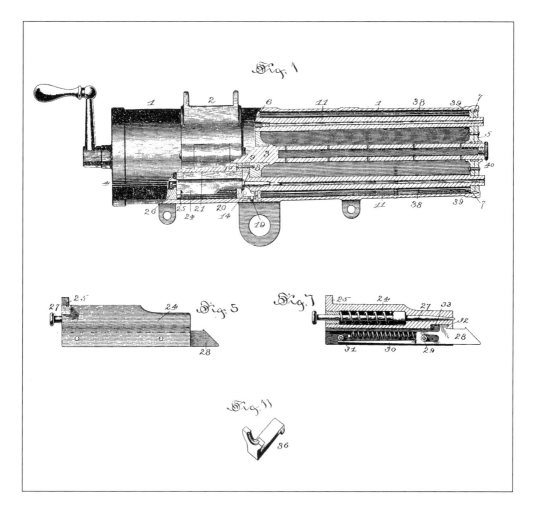

This patent, granted to R.J. Gatling, covered improved extraction and ejection of fired cartridge cases and the use of a water jacket to prevent overheating of the barrels during prolonged firing.

An ejector (36) was fitted to each barrel and started the extraction of the fired case. This was intended to improve the extraction.

The extractor (28) was greatly increased in size to strengthen it. A coil spring housed in the bolt (24) provided the tension necessary to make the claw grasp the rim of the cartridge.

The "cooling fluid" jacket (1) resembled the barrel jacket adopted by the U.S. Navy, but was fitted with seals to keep the coolant out of the locks. This jacket rotated with the barrels and was filled or emptied "from around the barrels."

United States Patent No. 499,534
June 13, 1893

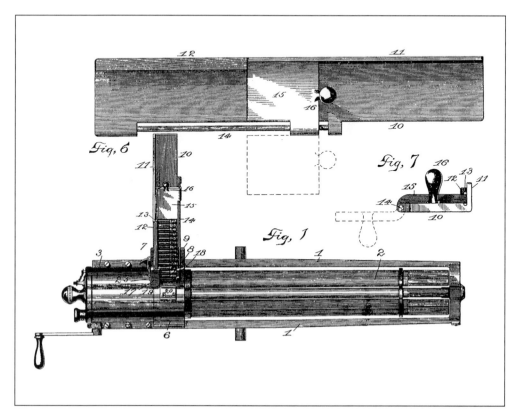

This improved feed tray was invented by R.J. Gatling. Loose cartridges, from the 20-round box, were placed on the upper portion of the tray. A follower was pivoted to the front of the gun to permit these rounds to slide toward the gun's breech. The follower (15) was mounted on a guide rod (14); as gravity and the natural vibration of the Gatling Gun being fired moved the follower closer to the breech, it forced the rims of the cartridges into a groove (12) in the tray. This properly aligned the cartridges to be picked up by the bolts and chambered.

Gatling suggested that the guide rod could be made to extend the entire length of the front edge of the feed tray. His theory was that the cartridges could be loaded quicker if they were simply placed loose on the feed tray and the follower forced them into the proper position.

No known examples of Gatling Guns with this feed device are known to exist.

United States Patent No. 502,185
July 25, 1893

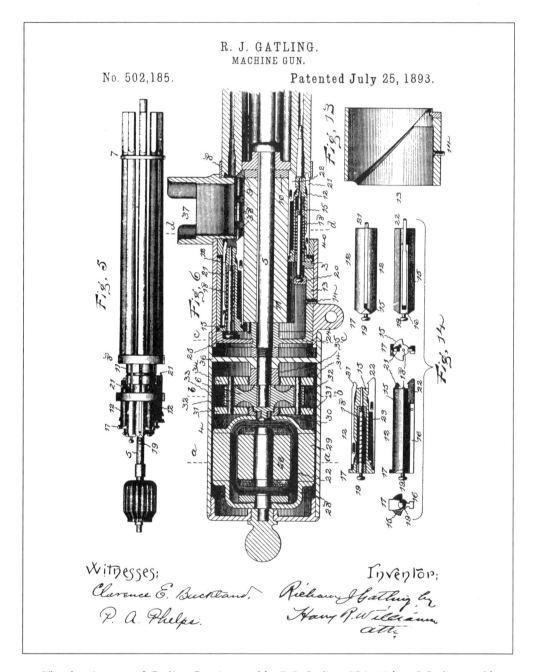

The electric powered Gatling Gun invented by R.J. Gatling. This 10-barrel Gatling could fire up to 3,000 rounds per minute. Unlike the Crocker-Wheeler electric Gatling of 1890, the motor was contained within the breech cover.

United States Patent No. 502,882
August 8, 1893

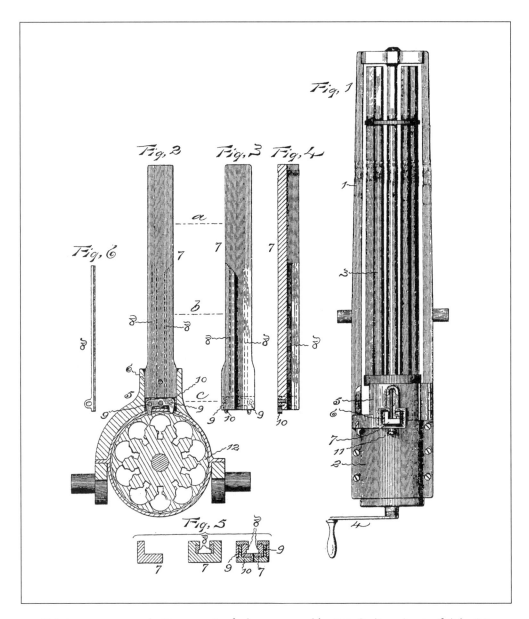

This improvement to the Bruce gravity feed was patented by R.J. Gatling. A pair of slides (8) was installed in the grooves of the feed that held the cartridges by their rims. A caming lever (10) at the base of the feed alternately moved one slide up and the other down; this would clear dust and debris from the grooves and prevent the rims of the cartridges from binding in the modified Bruce feed.

No recorded commercial production of this feed device was undertaken by the Gatling Gun Company or Colt's.

United States Patent No. 504,516
September 5, 1893

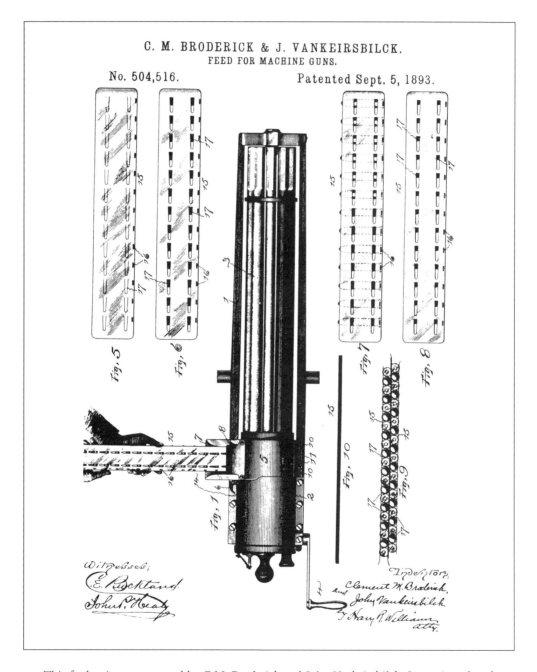

This feed strip was patented by C.M. Broderick and John Vankeirsbilck. It was introduced with the Model 1893 Gatling Gun. This feed system did not work well; all U.S. Army guns with this system were altered to the Bruce Feed at Springfield Armory.

United States Patent No. 504,517
September 5, 1893

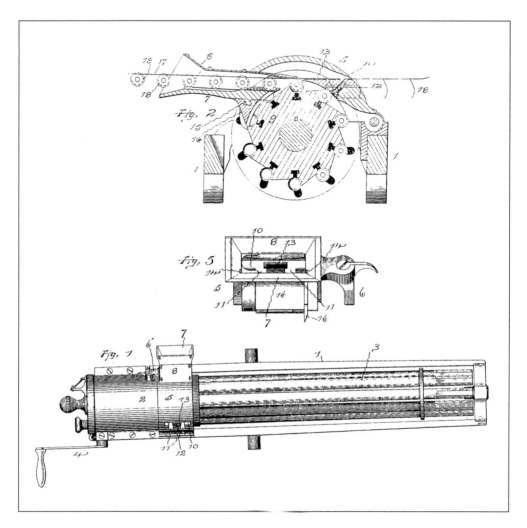

This patented "positive" feed hopper, designed by Clement M. Broderick and John Vankeirsbilck, was placed into production as the Model 1893 Gatling Gun. In practice, the feed strips were to be unreliable. All Model 1893 Gatlings purchased by the United States Army were altered to the reliable Bruce feed.

A metallic feed strip held the cartridges beneath the strip in spring fingers. As the Gatling's crank was rotated, this feed strip moved from left to right, delivering a cartridge to the bolt for chambering in the barrel in the uppermost barrel.

This patented feed hopper held the strip in place; empty strips were ejected from the right side of the gun. Several feed strips could be linked together to provide sustained rapid fire.

When the design failed under service conditions, the Gatling Gun Company blamed the problem on the feed strips manufactured by Springfield Armory.

United States Patent No. 504,831
September 12, 1893

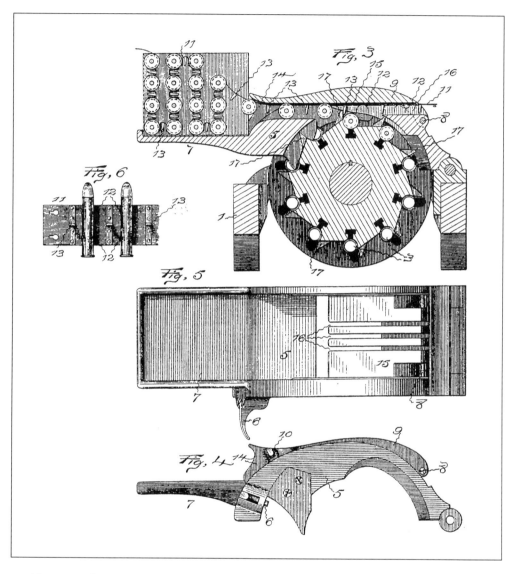

This patent by R.J. Gatling was designed to develop a more positive feed for the Gatling Gun. Gatling described this feed as being "infallible" in his description of the feed mechanism submitted to the patent office.

Gatling designed a flexible belt to hold the ammunition; it was mounted in a feed case on the left side of the gun. Flexible steel fingers held the cartridges in place on the belt until the bolts stripped them into the chambers of the barrels. Several belts could be linked together to permit continuous rapid fire from a Gatling Gun fitted with this feed device.

No serial production of Gatling Guns with this feed resulted from this invention.

United States Patent No. 550,262
November 26, 1895

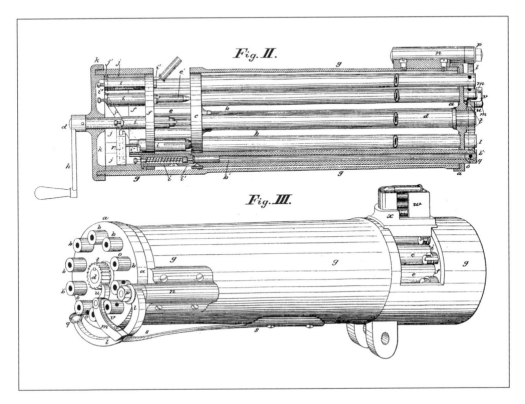

This automatic adaptation of the Gatling Gun was developed by Carl J. Ehbets, an employee of Colt's Patent Fire Arms Manufacturing Company. The first round was fired by turning the rear-mounted crank. The following rounds were fired automatically by the action of powder gasses escaping through a port in the barrel near the muzzle. Their pressure moved the lever (l) to rotate the barrels by the resulting action of a pawl and rachet (m, u and t). The lever then returned to close the port until the powder gasses repeated the operation. This machine gun used a top-mounted gravity feed.

Ehbets assigned the patent rights to his employer, but no commercial production resulted from his invention. Smaller and lighter machine guns were already in production at the time his patent was granted.

AN 1865 ADVERTISEMENT

GATLING'S
IMPROVED BATTERY GUN.

The main characteristic of this invention is, a gun having a series of barrels with a carrier and lock cylinder rigidly fastened to the main shaft, and rotating simultaneously and continuously, by means of a crank, the cartridges being fed into the cavities of the carrier from feed boxes, thence driven endwise into the rear ends of the barrels, then exploded, and the empty cartridge cases withdrawn, without any pause in the operation.

It is not necessary to describe the construction and operation of the invention in detail ; suffice it to say, the foregoing practical results - of loading and firing incessantly - are produced by the simplest kind of mechanism, there being less parts about the gun than in the Springfield Musket.

The gun can be discharged at the rate of *two hundred shots per minute*, and it bears the same relation to other fire arms that McCormack's Reaper does to the sickle, or the Sewing Machine to the common needle. It will, no doubt, be the means of producing a great revolution in the art of warfare, from the fact, that a few men with it, can perform the work of a regiment.

One of the valuable features of this arm is, there is no recoil which can effect the accuracy of its aim. When the gun is once sighted at a given object, say at the battery of an enemy, the same can be maintained at the will of the operator, until thousands of discharges take place. This is a matter of great practical importance, inasmuch as it supercedes, in a great degree, that random shooting which ordinarily occurs in the smoke and excitement of battle. A lateral train motion of the gun may be kept up, if desired, while the same is being discharged, so that a perfect sheet of balls, as it were, can be made to sweep a section of a circle within its range.

There is no escape of gas at the breech of the gun ; all the force of the powder is, therefore, expended in giving velocity to the ball ; hence the initial velocity and penetration of balls discharged from this gun are greater than that of most arms of the same calibre. A consideration of the very first importance in this improvement is, that every cartridge must be either discharged or withdrawn from the barrels, precluding the possibility of such results as were shown on the battle field at Gettysburg, where of the 27,574 muskets collected after the battle, 24,000 were found loaded ; 12,000 of which contained two loads, and 6,000, (or 20 per cent) were charged with from three to ten loads each, the cartridges often times being loaded without breaking them, and many inserted with the ball down first.

The gun is light and easily transported ; is simple in its construction strong and durable, and not at all liable to get out of order from use.

Two sizes of the gun are now being manufactured by the Cooper Fire Arms Manufacturing Company, Frankford, Philadelphia, Pa. One size discharges 58-100 inch calibre balls, and weighs 225 pounds, and the other one inch calibre leaden balls of 9 oz. in weight. The smaller size gun has a range of about one mile, and the larger size upwards of two miles.

R. J. GATLING, Patentee,
INDIANAPOLIS, IND.

August 17th, 1865.

This broadside was published on August 17, 1865. It offers Gatling Guns assembled by the Cooper Fire Arms Manufacturing Company of Philadelphia. Two sizes are offered: .58 Rimfire and 1". Gatling was still a resident of Indianapolis; Colt's had not yet assumed the manufacturing rights to his gun.

THE MODEL 1866 GATLING GUN

A 6-barrel, 1" caliber Model 1866 Gatling Gun, as manufactured by Colt's. This is a later production gun; the front of the frame has been arched to lessen the chance of a bullet striking it accidentally. The centrally mounted sights are shown, as is the artillery-style field carriage. Since there was no provision for traversing the gun, canister shot was developed for this 1" Gatling. This drawing originally appeared in the *Scientific American* on January 12, 1867.

THE MODEL 1866 GATLING GUN

This model 1866 6-barrel 1" Gatling Gun, on a Broadwell "all-metal" carriage, was tested by the U.K. during 1871. The magazine is shown inserted into the hopper on the left side of the breech.

The same Gatling, from the breech. The rear-mounted crank marks this as a Gatling made in Vienna, Austria, by Ed. A. Paget & Co. The British criticized the workmanship of this gun. Colt's did the same. Paget & Company was in great financial difficulty during 1871.

THE BRITISH TRIAL GUN OF 1867

On March 7, 1867, the British government tested a 6-barrel 1" Gatling Gun at Shoeburyness. The gun was taken to England by Major General John Love and Lewis Broadwell, acting as European sales agents for the Gatling Gun Company. Both ball and multi-ball cartridges were used in competition with an Armstrong 9-pounder field gun. *The Illustrated London News* carried the report of this trial on March 23, 1867. This newspaper report concluded with, "The Gatling Gun is a formidable weapon; and for trenches or a breach, and for street fighting, would be execution. The little amount of recoil and the consequent advantage of retaining a tolerably accurate direction after being once sighted, might prove a valuable element, and, in certain cases, would give it an advantage not possessed by ordinary cannon, which have to be resighted after each discharge." The drawing above accompanied the newspaper report.

THE SWISS MODEL 1868 GATLING GUN

This Model 1868 Gatling Gun was a 6-barrel 1" gun, used by Switzerland. It is mounted on an artillery pattern field carriage. Both ball and multi-ball (canister) ammunition was loaded in Switzerland. These cartridges, while appearing to be rimfire, are internally primed centerfire. They are similar to the 1" ball cartridges loaded at Frankford Arsenal during 1866. The Swiss also produced dummy ball cartridges for this Gatling.

TEST TARGETS, AUSTRIA
1868 and 1869

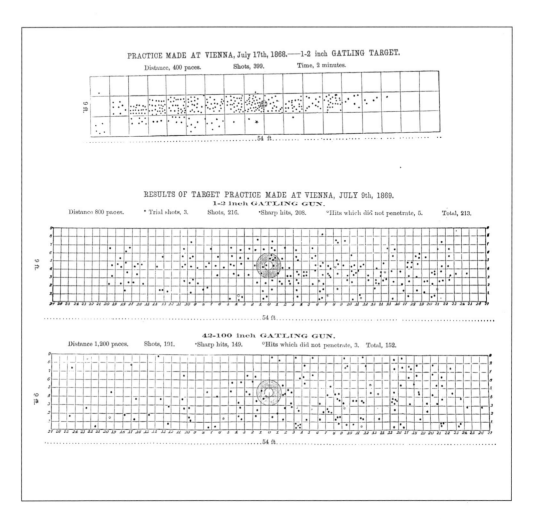

The Austrian government conducted two trials of Gatling Guns at Vienna. The first, on July 17, 1868, was conducted using a .50-70, 10-barreled Gatling. In two minutes, 399 rounds were fired. The target was 9 feet by 54 feet and set up at 400 paces. The second trial was held on July 9, 1869. Two Gatlings were tested this time. After firing 3 aiming rounds, 216 shots were fired from a .50-70, 10-barreled Gatling in one minute. A total of 213 "hits" were recorded at 800 paces. The second Gatling used in this trial was a Russian model, chambering the .42 Berdan cartridge. At 1,200 paces, 191 rounds were fired; the "hits" totaled 152. Both of these targets were the same size as that used during 1868, but had much larger bull's-eyes.

TEST TARGETS, BADEN
1869

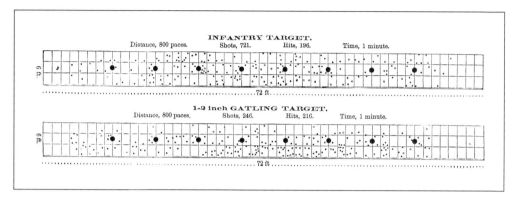

During August of 1869, the Kingdom of Baden conducted a trial of a .50-70, 10-barreled Gatling Gun against 100 infantrymen armed with the Dreyse "needle gun." They each fired for one minute at a series of eight bull's-eyes on a target measuring 6' x 72'. The 100 soldiers fired a total of 721 shots and registered 196 "hits." The single Gatling fired 246 shots; 216 were recorded as "hits." The distance was 800 paces. This trial took place on the army firing range at Karlsruhe.

TEST TARGET, UNITED STATES
1869

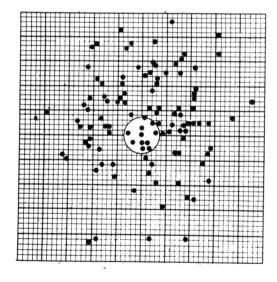

This target was shot on November 3, 1869, at Hartford, Connecticut. A 1" Gatling Gun was used to fire 110 shots, scoring 110 "hits." The target was 10" x 10" with an 18" diameter Bull's-Eye; the range was 500 yards. The 1" ball cartridge was used in this demonstration.

THE MODEL 1870 GATLING GUN
Turkish Contract

A Model 1870 Gatling Gun chambered for a rifle ("musket") cartridge. The rear-mounted crank on this early model indicates production by Ed. A. Paget & Company in Vienna, Austria.

Ammunition used was the .58 Turkish Snider cartridge. Turkey contracted for a quantity of these Gatlings in 1870 for their army and navy. Colt's assigned this contract to Paget & Company. The curved magazine was introduced during 1871 in U.S. Army service, about the same time the Turkish contract guns were being delivered. The carriage is the standard heavy field pattern, typical of the 1870s.

THE RUSSIAN GORLOFF

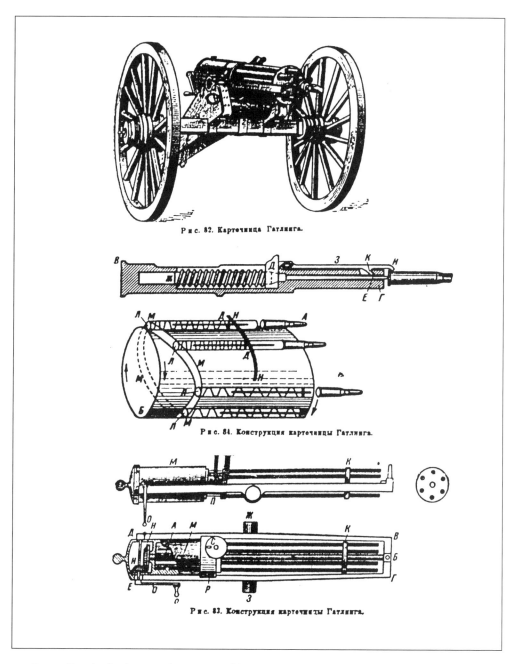

Рис. 82. Картечница Гатлинга.

Рис. 84. Конструкция картечницы Гатлинга.

Рис. 83. Конструкция картечницы Гатлинга.

From a Russian book on machine guns published in Moscow in 1929. Note that the cartridge case in the bolt appears to be 7.62 x 54mm Rimmed. Were .42 Berdan Gatlings and Gorloffs altered to this cartridge after 1891? The drawing of the mechanism shows the feed plate for a Broadwell drum.

THE MODEL 1871 GATLING GUN

The only 1" Gatling Gun with 10 barrels purchased by the U.S. Army. This gun, serial number 121, was the last 1" Gatling manufactured by Colt's. The gun was produced during 1871; the U.S. Army carried it on their records as a Model 1871. This gun was still "in service" during 1895. The curved magazine is shown in place; it was adopted as standard in 1871.

THE MODEL 1871 GATLING GUN

The .50-70 caliber 10-barrel Model 1871 Gatling Gun, on L.W. Broadwell's "all-metal" carriage. Note that the wheels were still wooden. This model was offered in five- or six-barrel patterns at the purchaser's request. This was the first Gatling to accept a curved magazine. The magazine is not shown in this drawing.

THE BRITISH MODEL 1871 GATLING GUN

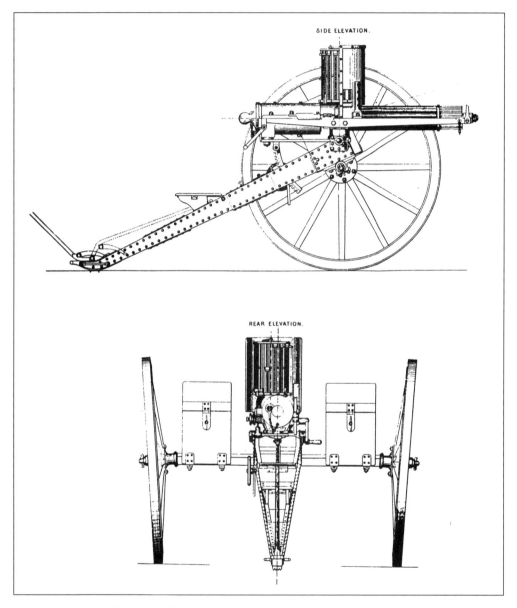

This is typical of the .45 caliber 10-barreled Gatling Guns manufactured by Sir William G. Armstrong & Company at Newcastle-on-Tyne, England. The field carriage is an "all-metal" Broadwell design. A pair of axle-mounted chests held extra Broadwell drums and the gunner's implements. The rack-and-pinion elevation design was faster than the jack screw on Colt's products. The Broadwell drum was protected by a steel shield, a feature found only on Armstrong's Gatlings. The hand spike, on the trail, was hinged rather than removable as in United States Army service.

THE U.S. NAVY MODEL 1871 GATLING GUN

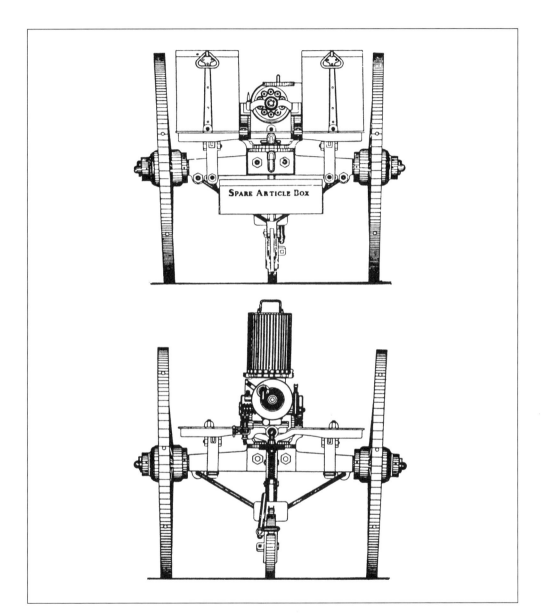

This long 10-barreled .50-70 Model 1871 Gatling Gun is mounted on a "steel" landing party carriage. This light carriage retained wooden wheels. The gunner's seat pivots on the trail, rather than being hinged as on the U.S. Army Model 1875 carriage. The axle-mounted ammunition chests held additional Broadwell drums. Appendages were carried in a chest located beneath the axle. A lunette ring was provided for hauling behind a limber. The third wheel, at the rear of the trail, enhanced maneuvering by members of the landing party.

THE U.S. NAVY MODEL 1871 GATLING GUN

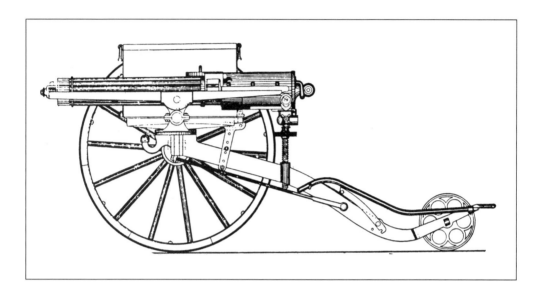

This long 10-barreled .50-70 Model 1871 Gatling Gun is mounted on a "steel" landing party carriage. The gunner's seat pivots on the trail, rather than being hinged as on the U.S. Army Model 1875 carriage. The pair of axle-mounted Broadwell drum chests could be tilted forward to give the gunner more room. The retaining strap is visible below the rear of the chest. The chest for appendages, located beneath the axle, is omitted in this drawing. The hinged pattern hand-spike is shown in the traveling position, as is the gunner's seat. The third wheel, at the rear of the trail, enhanced maneuvering by members of the landing party.

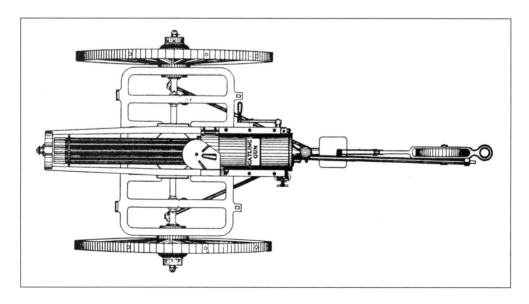

THE FIRING CYCLE OF A MODEL 1871 GATLING GUN

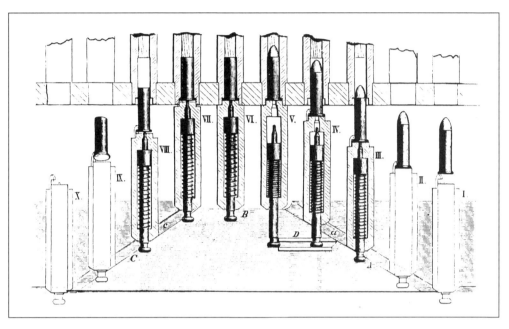

This Springfield Armory drawing shows the firing cycle for the 10-barreled .50-70 Model 1871 Gatling Gun. As the barrels rotate, they are loaded at positions I, II and III, the firing pin is "cocked" at positions IV and V, and the gun fires at position VI. The spent cartridge is ejected at position IX. As a note, the cartridge at position IX was not shown free of the extractor until the later versions of this drawing were published. This cycle is identical for all 10-barreled Gatling Guns.

THE U.S. ARMY GATLING GUN
CREW POSITIONS

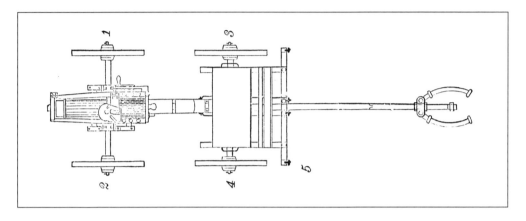

The five-man Gatling Gun crew position, "on the march," ca.1871. Two horses drew the Gatling and limber; the men marched in the positions indicated by the numbers.

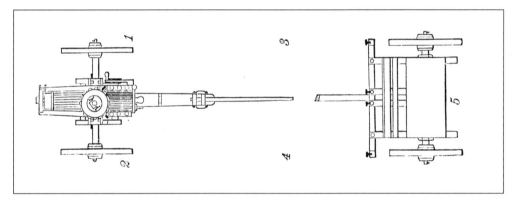

When in action, the horses were tethered away from the Gatling; an assistant gunner (No. 2) stood by the side of the Gatling and loaded it while the gunner (No. 1) rotated the crank. The second assistant gunner (No. 3) aimed the Gatling. The fourth and fifth men acted as ammunition bearers, bringing loaded Broadwell Drums from the limber chest to the assistant gunners. Nos. 2, 4 and 5 rotated places with each other as the gun was fired.

SCHUYLER, HARTLEY & GRAHAM CATALOGUE
1872

CATALOGUE

OF

MUNITIONS OF WAR.

COMPRISING

HEAVY ORDNANCE, LIGHT ARTILLERY,

GATLING GUNS,

ALL SYSTEMS OF BREECH-LOADING SMALL ARMS, PISTOLS,
SWORDS, CUTLASSES, ETC.

AMMUNITION:

PROJECTILES FOR HEAVY ORDNANCE AND FIELD AR
CARTRIDGES OF ALL CLASSES, POWDER IN LARG
AND SMALL QUANTITIES.

EQUIPMENTS:

UNIFORMS COMPLETE FOR OFFICERS AND SOLDIERS, K
HAVERSACKS, CAMP CHESTS, TENTS, MARQUEE
FLAGS, GUIDONS, ETC.

REGIMENTS AND COMPANIES COMPLETELY E(

SCHUYLER, HARTLEY & GRAHA
19 MAIDEN LANE, 20 & 22 JOHN ST
NEW YORK.

CATALOGUE OF MUNITIONS OF WAR.   3

SCHUYLER, HARTLEY & GRAHAM

FIELD AND LIGHT ARTILLERY.

Parrott 20 pound iron rifle gun.
    do.   10 pound   "   "   "
Napoleon 12 pound brass gun.
Howitzer 12 pound brass.
United States 6 pound brass gun.

Batteries complete for the above, comprising Caison, Battery-wagon,
Forge, Limber-chest, implements, tools, and horse equipments.

Mountain-Howitzer, for use on small carriage or mule.
Boat Howitzer.
Cohorn Mortar.

PROJECTILES.

Shot, shell, shrapnel, canister and grape furnished for all the above.

GATLING BATTERY,

Adopted by the Governments of the United States, Russia, Turkey,
Great Britain and Spain.

One inch calibre, six or ten barrels.
Three quarter inch calibre, six or ten barrels.
Smaller size ten barrel calibre, to order, to suit musket ammunition of all
nations.
    Light gun adapted to either camel or mule, weighing one hundred and
twenty pounds.

    Carriages and proper equipments for all the above. Berdan's central
fire reloading cartridges for all calibres of the Gatling gun.

EXTRACT FROM REPORT OF COMMISSION OF BRITISH OFFICERS.

28th Oct., 1870.

" The results of the recent enquiry have fully satisfied the Committee
of the expediency of introducing a certain proportion of these machine
guns to act as auxiliaries to the other arms of the service, and of the several
designs which have been submitted for their consideration, including those
that have been under trial, they are persuaded that the Gatling gun is the
best adapted to meet all military requirements."

The front cover and page 3 of the 1872 Schuyler, Hartley & Graham *Catalogue of Munitions of War* from 1872. This New York City exporter sold new and used military arms throughout the world. Gatling Gun sales efforts continued when the firm became Hartley & Graham.

THE U.S. ARMY MODEL 1874 GATLING GUN

The Model 1874 Gatling Gun, as purchased by the U.S. Army. This was the first .45-70 Gatling. It was manufactured with 10 long (32") barrels. The feed hopper, to accept the Model 1874 Magazine is visible on the left rear of the breech housing. The improved oscillator is below the breech. The mount is a field carriage; the gunner's seat is in the traveling position. Eight of these Gatlings were purchased from Colt's for the army.

NOMENCLATURE OF THE MODEL 1874 GATLING GUN
.45-70-500

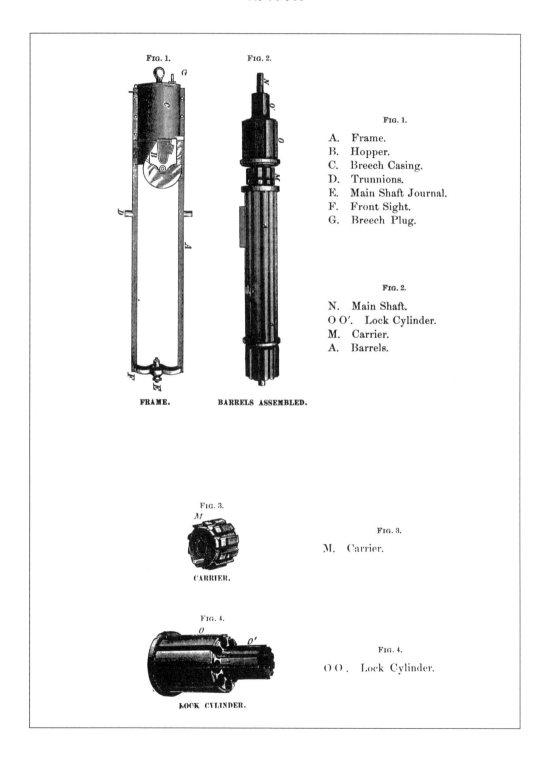

FIG. 1.

A. Frame.
B. Hopper.
C. Breech Casing.
D. Trunnions.
E. Main Shaft Journal.
F. Front Sight.
G. Breech Plug.

FIG. 2.

N. Main Shaft.
O O′. Lock Cylinder.
M. Carrier.
A. Barrels.

FIG. 3.

M. Carrier.

FIG. 4.

O O. Lock Cylinder.

FRAME.   BARRELS ASSEMBLED.

CARRIER.

LOCK CYLINDER.

NOMENCLATURE OF THE MODEL 1874 GATLING GUN
.45-70-500

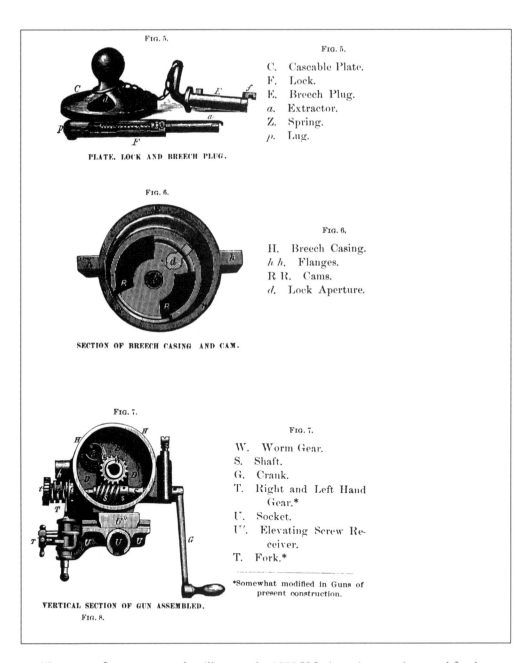

FIG. 5.

PLATE, LOCK AND BREECH PLUG.

FIG. 6.

SECTION OF BREECH CASING AND CAM.

FIG. 7.

VERTICAL SECTION OF GUN ASSEMBLED.
FIG. 8.

FIG. 5.

C. Cascable Plate.
F. Lock.
E. Breech Plug.
a. Extractor.
Z. Spring.
p. Lug.

FIG. 6,

H. Breech Casing.
h h. Flanges.
R R. Cams.
d. Lock Aperture.

FIG. 7.

W. Worm Gear.
S. Shaft.
G. Crank.
T. Right and Left Hand Gear.*
U. Socket.
U'. Elevating Screw Receiver.
T. Fork.*

*Somewhat modified in Guns of present construction.

These seven figures were used to illustrate the 1875 U.S. Army inspector's manual for the officers detailed to the Colt factory to accept the Model 1874 Gatling Gun for military service. No drawing of the complete Gatling was included. The only other Gatling-related illustrations were the appendages to be delivered with each gun.

COSTS OF THE MODEL 1874 GATLINGS

PRICE LISTS

OF THE

GATLING GUNS AND ARMY REVOLVERS.

❖❖❖

GATLING GUN

Components.	Long Barrel.	Short Barrel.	Components.	Long Barrel.	Short Barrel.
Adjustable screw nut........	$4 84	$4 84	Lock extractor screws.......	06	06
10 Barrels, @ $27 and $12......	270 00	120 00	Lock extractor sleeve... ...	7 44	7 44
Breech casing...	67 20	67 20	2 Lock extractor sleeve scr.,		
6 Breech casing screws, @ 66c,	3 96	3 96	@ 6c,.....................	12	12
10 Bushings, @ 84c,...........	8 32	8 32	10 Lock main springs, @ 44c,.	4 36	4 36
Cartridge carrier............	47 60	47 60	10 Lock nuts, @ 82c,.........	8 20	8 20
Cartridge shell ejector.......	13 40	13 40	10 Lock tubes, @ $11.66,......	116 54	116 54
3 Cartridge shell ejector scr.,			Main shaft.................	53 16	28 16
@ 6c,..................	18	18	Oscillating thread nut and		
Cartridge shell extractor			washer	35 64	35 64
block	3 36	3 36	Rear guide nut..............	4 76	4 76
2 Cartridge shell extractor			Rear plate for barrels........	21 72	21 72
block screws, @ 48c, ...	96	96	Rear sight.................	13 40	13 40
Cascable plate................	18 60	18 60	Rear sight screws...	1 04	1 04
Cocking device........	25 12	25 12	Spiral cam.................	49 68	49 68
Crank...	9 52	9 52	2 Spiral cam screws, @ 48c,...	96	96
Crank latch................	3 60	3 60	2 Trunnions, @ $2.90,........	5 80	5 80
Crank shaft................	6 44	6 44	Washer for front end of		
Diaphragm.................	16 52	16 52	main shaft..............	76	76
Dowel pins.................	1 00	1 00	Worm	12 92	12 92
10 Extractor hooks, @ $2.50,.	24 92	24 92	Worm gear.................	10 32	10 32
10 Firing pins, @ $2.54,......	25 36	25 36			
Front cap.................	5 24	5 24			
Front plate for barrels.......	12 64	12 64			
Front sight.................	4 52	4 52	APPENDAGES.		
Front sight screws...........	48	48			
Gas collar..................	1 60	1 60	Adjusting screw wrench.....	28	28
Gun frame.................	75 24	50 24	Brass wiping rod.............	2 32	2 32
Hopper.....................	58 32	58 32	Clamp for worm gear........	3 96	3 96
Hopper hinge...............	9 80	9 80	Lock screw driver...........	1 00	1 00
Hopper hinge pin..	1 72	1 72	Pin wrench................	56	56
2 Hopper hinge screws, @ 48c,	96	96	Rear guide nut wrench......	80	80
Hopper latch................	6 32	6 32	Shell driver...	3 44	3 44
Hopper latch screws..........	06	06	Small screw driver...........	56	56
Lock cylinder........	85 40	85 40	T Screw driver........ ...	4 00	4 00
2 Lock cylinder screws, @ 12c,	24	24			
Lock extractor..............	22 76	22 76	Total.........	1200 00	1000 00

This "price list" of the component parts of the Model 1874 long and short barreled Gatling Gun was taken from the 1875 inspector's manual. The parts and appendages are priced for the Gatling Gun; no carriage costs are included. A note on the following page explained, "These prices are, by order of the War Department, to be employed in charging arms and parts of arms on muster and pay rolls, etc;" in other words, if the soldier broke it, he bought it.

THE U.S. NAVY MODEL 1874 GATLING GUN

The Model 1874 U.S. Navy .45-70 Gatling Gun, on a lightweight "steel" carriage designed for use by Naval Landing Parties. Tow lines were affixed to the cross bar on the trail for towing by sailors. The frames on either side of the Gatling were designed to hold magazines; they could be tipped forward to give the gunner more room to work. The carriage is "all metal" except for the wooden wheels. This Gatling was designed for the Model 1874 Magazine, instead of the earlier Broadwell Drum. The third wheel of the Model 1871 carriage was not incorporated into the Model 1874 carriage. A lunette ring was provided for hauling behind a limber.

THE MODEL 1874 CAMEL GUN

The short (18") 10-barrel Model 1874 Gatling Gun was designed to accept the Broadwell Drum. The "Camel Gun" name was a great publicity and sales device. The standard U.S. service mount was somewhat more mundane: the Cavalry Cart or a tripod.

THE MODEL 1874 CAMEL GUN

The Model 1874 Camel Gun on the wood and bronze tripod mount. The Broadwell Drum is in place; the gun is ready to fire. The front and rear sights were moved to the right side of the frame with the introduction of the Model 1874 Gatlings.

THE MODEL 1874 CAMEL GUN

A suggested form of transporting the Model 1874 Camel Gun, together with its tripod and Broadwell Drums. Since the Gatling alone weighed 135 pounds when the tripod and two Broadwell Drums (each loaded with 400 rounds) were added, this was a heavy load for the two gunners. Additional magazines were transported on yokes.

A much more practical method of transporting the Model 1874 Camel Gun (or any Gatling). The opposite side of this pack saddle held the tripod and another pair of Broadwell Drums. The saddle could be adapted to carry either long- or short-barreled Gatling Guns.

THE MODEL 1875 GATLING GUN

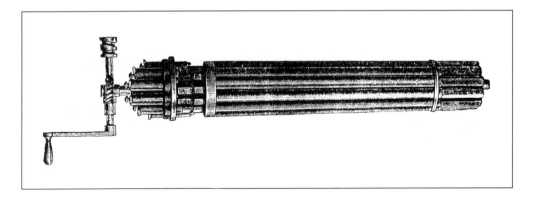

The ten .45-70 barrels, locks (bolts), and the crank of the Model 1875 Gatling Gun, removed from the frame and breech housing of the gun. The U.S. Army purchased 44 of this model Gatling.

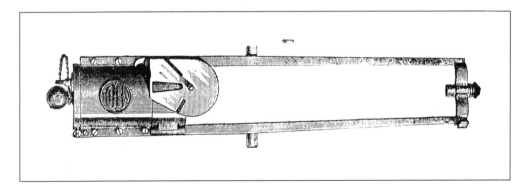

The frame and breech housing of the Model 1875 Gatling Gun. The flat plate on the breech housing accepted the Broadwell Drum. The headspace adjustment screw is in the center of the front of the frame. The trunnions, for mounting, are on either side of the frame. A circular plate behind the drum magazine plate carried the Colt's name and relevant patent data.

THE MODEL 1875 U.S. NAVY GATLING GUN

This Model 1875 U.S. Navy Gatling Gun introduced the bronze barrel jacket. The length of the barrels was between that of the Model 1874 Camel Gun and the Army's long Gatlings. The Aiming Bar was introduced with the Model 1879 Gatling, so the tripod mount postdates the gun.

THE U.S. NAVY GATLING GUN
CREW POSITIONS

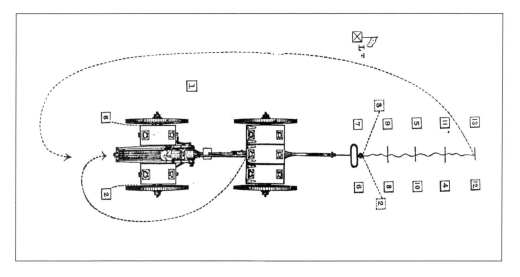

The 13-man gun crew was expected to use "drag ropes" to haul the long-barreled Gatling Gun into position on land. The manual notes that while on the march, a duplicate crew may be required to offer relief to the gun crew.

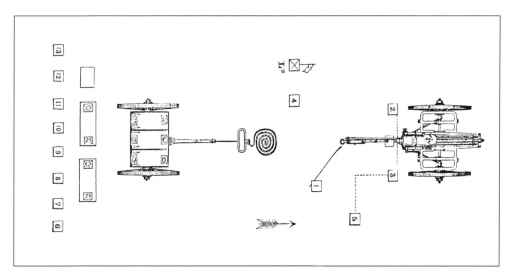

Once in position, the gun crew arranged themselves to provide a constant supply of filled Broadwell drum magazines from the chests on the limber. The ammunition supply on the limber was not in drums; each of the three "caisson boxes" held 1,320 rounds in the 20-round boxes. If stored as loose cartridges, 1,600 rounds could be held in each chest. Careful stowing of loose cartridges increased the rated capacity of each chest to 2,100 rounds. From the 1875 U.S. Navy manual.

THE U.S. ARMY MODEL 1876 GATLING GUN

The Model 1876 10-barrel .45-70 Gatling Gun, as purchased for issue to the United States Army. The field carriage is of wood, with bronze and steel fittings. The gunner's seat is in the traveling position on the trail. The handspike is in position on the left side of the trail. This was the last series of Gatlings fitted with the cam-operated oscillator below the cascabel.

THE MODEL 1876 GATLING GUN

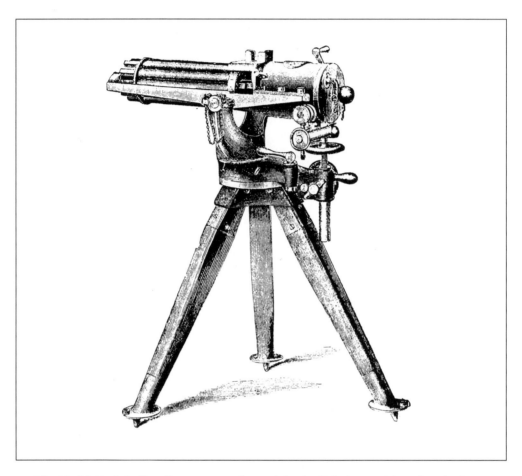

The Model 1876 Gatling Gun was manufactured for the U.S. Army with 10 barrels chambered for the .45-70 cartridge. It was the first Gatling to have a center-mounted hopper to accept the gravity feed magazine. It was offered by Colt's on a variety of mountings, including the bronze and wood tripod shown above.

GATLING GUNS AT THE 1876 INTERNATIONAL
CENTENNIAL EXPOSITION

Gatling Guns on display at the U.S. Army exhibit at the Philadelphia International Centennial Exposition. Also on exhibit, are a .45-70 Gatling on the Cavalry Cart drawn by a single horse (far left) and a 1" Gatling (center). To the right of the 1" Gatling is an Ager "coffee mill" machine gun from the Civil War. Ager-type cartridges were used in the Model 1862 Gatling Gun.

A GATLING GUN COMPANY ADVERTISING CARD

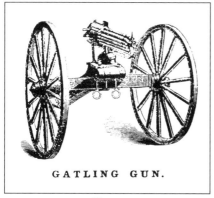

GATLING GUN.

The Gatling Gun.

As a practical military machine gun, the GATLING has no equal. It fires from 800 to 1,000 shots per minute, has great accuracy, and the larger calibres have an effective range of over two miles. The following calibres are made: .42, .43, .45, .50, .55, .65, .75, and one inch. It has been adopted by nearly all the principal governments of the world.

Gatling Gun Company,
HARTFORD, CONN., U. S. A.

Front   *Back*

This advertising card was handed out to visitors at the 1876 International Centennial Exposition held in Philadelphia. On September 27, the inventor was awarded with the only medal presented for "machine guns" at the Exposition.

THE MODEL 1877 GATLING

A long 10-barrel .45-70 Model 1877 Gatling Gun ready to travel. The lunette ring has been attached to the hook on the limber. The limber chest held filled magazines and the implements. The limber pole is not shown full length in this drawing.

A long 10-barrel Model 1877 Gatling Gun ready to fire, once a magazine has been inserted. The cam-operated oscillator is below the cascabel. The hinged seat for the gunner is visible on the trail.

GATLING GUN COMPANY ADVERTISEMENT

New Model Five Barreled Gatling Gun.   Weight 97 Pounds.

As a practical military machine gun, the GATLING has no equal.   It fires from 800 to 1,000 shots per minute, has great accuracy, and the larger calibres have an effective range of over two miles.   The following calibres are made: .42, .43, .45, .50, .55, .65, .75, and 1 inch.   It has been adopted by nearly all the principal governments of the world.   Address,

Gatling Gun Company,
HARTFORD, CONN., U. S. A.

The Model 1877 Bulldog Gatling, as advertised in 1877 by the sales company. This model introduced the rear-mounted crank. It was the last model without the "aiming bar" that was introduced with the Model 1879. The field carriage pictured was not the usual mount; both tripods and Cavalry Carts were used by the United States Army. The cartridges advertised were .42 Berdan (Russian), .43 Spanish, .45-70, .50-70, .55, .65 (British Navy), .75 and 1".

THE MODEL 1877 BULLDOG GATLING GUN

This 10-barrel Model 1877 Bulldog Gatling Gun has been fitted with the Bruce feed patented in 1881. A special version of the Bruce feed was developed to fit Gatlings designed to use the gravity feed magazines adopted as standard in 1874. This is the pattern utilized with this Gatling. The Bruce feed was loaded from a standard box of 20 cartridges; the ammunition was in two parallel columns. When the first column was empty, the other began to feed into the Gatling. This was the most successful feed device designed for the Gatling. It use spanned the .45-70, .30-40, .30-03 and .30-06 cartridges. *The Scientific American* duly reported this innovative feed device in 1881. The Gatling is mounted on a lightweight field carriage. The chests on either side of the Gatling held ammunition, a spare Bruce feed, the gunner's implements, etc. They hinged forward to provide more room for the gunner to turn the crank.

THE MODEL 1877 BULLDOG GATLING GUN

The "standard" version of the Model 1877 Bulldog Gatling Gun had five barrels. The metal capped wooden tripod legs were inserted into sockets; they were not hinged, but detachable. No aiming bar was provided with this pattern Gatling. It took only the gravity feed introduced in 1874.

THE MODEL 1877 BULLDOG GATLING GUN

A 10-barrel Model 1877 "Bulldog" Gatling, on the tripod mount. The rear mounted crank and no Aiming Bar identify this model. The design of the tripod was improved over earlier patterns. This pattern Gatling was purchased by China in preference to the usual 5-barrel model. No magazine is shown in this 1880 drawing.

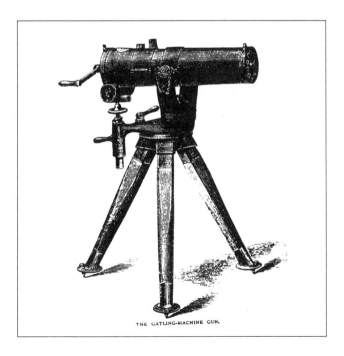

THE GATLING-MACHINE GUN.

THE U.S. NAVY MODEL 1877 GATLING GUN

A .45-70 10-barreled Model 1877 Gatling Gun, as purchased by the U.S. Navy. This gun used the Model 1874 Gravity Feed. The length of the gun was 36"; when mounted on this "cage" pattern deck mount, the height to the top of the Gatling was 48". This mount was but one of several "cone," "pedestal" or "cage" mounts that were bolted to the decks of naval vessels.

THE MODEL 1879 GATLING GUN

The 10-barrel "musket calibre" Model 1879 Gatling Gun, on a field carriage. The Aiming Bar and flexible yoke were introduced with the Model 1879 Gatling. This is an "export" Gatling; the U.S. Army did not purchase long Gatlings with barrel jackets until 1883. The gunner's seat, on the trail, is in the ready mode. This pattern aiming bar was used extensively on the British Gatlings.

THE 1879 POINTING BAR

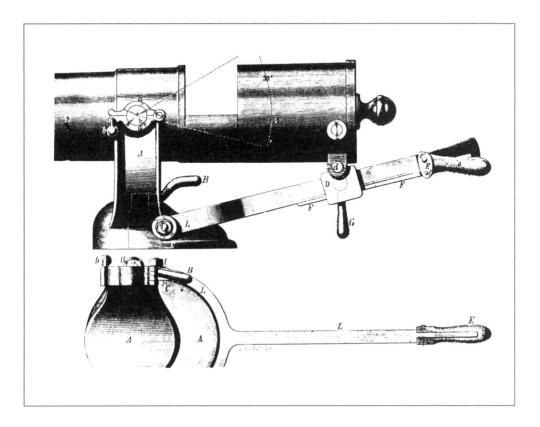

The 1879 improved "flexible yoke" pointing bar, from *The Scientific American*, allowed a wide latitude of traverse and elevation of the Gatling Gun. The "binder box" (D) could be locked by a lever (G) on the pointing bar (L) at the desired elevation. Elevation was limited to 15 degrees, while depression was restricted to 30 degrees. The yoke-mounted lever (B) was used to lock the gun in the desired traverse position. This system was much quicker than the prior screw method employed. When mounted on a field carriage, the center of the Gatling was $41^{3}/_{4}$" from the ground. The use of a tripod mount lowered the center to $39^{3}/_{4}$". Note that in the top view of the yoke (A) and traversing mechanism (C), the gun and binder box are not shown.

THE 1881 CHALLENGE
A NOTICE

The Gatling Gun
Many articles have recently appeared in the
press, claiming the superior advantages of the
Gardner and other machine guns over the
Gatling Gun.

In order to decide which is the best gun, the
undersigned offers to fire his gun (the Gatling)
against any other gun, on the following wagers,
viz:
First: $500 that the Gatling can fire more shots
in a given time, say one minute.
Second: $500 that the Gatling can give more hits
on a target, firing, say one minute — at a range of
800 or 1000 yards.
The winner to contribute the money won to some
charitable object.
The time and place for the trials to be mutually
agreed upon.

R.J. Gatling
of Hartford, Conn.

This challenge appeared in the *Army & Navy Journal* for August 27, 1881. A similar advertisement appeared in Great Britain during September 1881. This version offered the wager in pounds sterling and added, "Trials of the above character will do more to determine the efficiency of the guns than newspaper articles ever so cleverly written" to the last paragraph. According to the *Broad Arrow*, a similar military journal published in London on October 15, 1881, this challenge had not been answered. No response by Gardner, Nordenfeldt, et al was ever reported!

A GATLING GUN ADVERTISEMENT
1882

HARTLEY & GRAHAM,

17 & 19 MAIDEN LANE,

NEW YORK,

Ordnance & Ordnance Stores

For Army and Navy Use.

GATLING AND OTHER MACHINE GUNS.

BREECH AND MUZZLE LOADING RIFLES, of all makes and calibres.

METALLIC AMMUNITION of every description.

THE CELEBRATED PEABODY-MARTINI, REM-INGTON, SHARPS, BORCHARDT, and other BREECH-LOADING RIFLES.

WINCHESTER, BURGESS, and *THE* LEE MAGA-ZINE REPEATING ARMS.

SPRINGFIELD, ENFIELD, and *all* other MUZZLE-LOADING MUSKETS, in stock for immediate delivery.

SMITH & WESSON'S, COLT'S, HOOD'S, and other celebrated REVOLVERS, in every variety.

SABRES, BELTS and EQUIPMENTS.

Companies and Expeditions
Fitted out at short notice.

Aware of the demand for "machine guns," Hartley & Graham listed the Gatling Gun first in this 1882 advertisement for military arms. The ammunition offered was that produced by the Union Metallic Cartridge Company of Bridgeport, Connecticut.

THE MODEL 1883 GATLING GUN

The Model 1883 Gatling Gun fitted with an Accles Drum. This magazine held 104 rounds of .45-70 ammunition. For the next five years, the U.S. Government purchased only Gatlings with this pattern bronze barrel jacket. The crank could be moved to the rear to increase the rate of fire. The large, open yoke was used only with this model. The steel field carriage had bronze fittings and wooden wheels. The chests on either side of the gun held a total of four Accles feeds, the two rear sights, gunner's implements, and spare parts. There was a hinged seat for the gunner mounted on the trail.

THE MODEL 1883 GATLING GUN

A Model 1883 Gatling Gun adapted for the Accles Feed. This was also described as a "positive feed" but it was subject to failure if the brass magazine housing was dented. The illustration shows the extreme of elevation at which the Accles feed would function. The Gatling is mounted on a very light "all-metal" field carriage. A spare Accles Feed rests on the gunner's seat. Fired cartridge cases litter the ground beneath the Gatling.

THE MODEL 1883 GATLING GUN

A long 10-barreled Model 1883 Gatling Gun, fitted for the Accles drum, on a lightweight "all-metal" field carriage. Extra Accles feeds were carried in the axle mounted chests. This drawing showed that the Accles drum fed ammunition reliably when the Gatling was at its extreme of depression. This was the first "positive feed" designed for Colt's Gatling Guns.

THE MODEL 1883 GATLING GUN

A long 10-barreled Model 1883 Gatling Gun, fitted for the Accles drum, on a lightweight "all-metal" field carriage with a tubular axle. The carrying handle is visible at the top of the Accles feed. Three extra drums are on the ground. The pointing bar extends to the rear of the Gatling. The presence of front sights on each side of the barrel jacket indicate that this gun is chambered for the .45-70 cartridge. The right-side sights were used when the 500 grain bullet was fired; those on the left were for use with the lighter carbine bullet.

THE MODEL 1883 GATLING GUN

A long 10-barreled Gatling Gun, fitted for the Accles drum, on a lightweight field carriage. The trail is extremely short for a carriage designed to mount a long-barreled Gatling. The Colt/Gatling data plate is visible on the breech housing. In this example, the aiming bar is offset to the left rather than centered beneath the Gatling.

THE MODEL 1883 GATLING GUN

A tricycle field carriage was designed for the long 10-barreled Model 1883 Gatling Gun, fed by the Accles feed drum. A lightweight steel tripod is carried, folded, across the front of this unusual mount. The carrying handle is visible at the top of the Accles feed. A total of ten Accles drums were carried in the two axle-mounted chests. This carriage permitted firing the Gatling while advancing, provided the ground was fairly level. For transport over a distance, the striped pole was placed in position for horses to draw the Gatling. For shorter distances, drag ropes were affixed to the linchpins on each end of the axle. Manpower provided the muscle for movement with drag ropes. From the number of illustrations located, the Model 1883 Gatling Gun and Accles feed was of great interest to the public.

THE MODEL 1883 GATLING GUN

A long 10-barreled Model 1883 Gatling Gun, fed by the Accles drum, on a lightweight steel tripod. This tripod has the legs pivoted at the mounting plate to permit easy transport in the "folded" position. The carrying handle is visible at the top of the Accles feed. A spare drum is on the ground. Because the thin brass drum housing was subject to denting and therefore jamming, this was not the recommended storage practice. The aiming bar (mounted on the left side) extends to the rear of the Gatling. This is another .45-70 caliber Gatling Gun.

Once the tricycle field carriage was properly sited and high-angle fire was desired, the rear wheel was removed. The long 10-barreled Model 1883 Gatling Gun, with the Accles feed drum in place, could then rain bullets down on the target. A total of ten Accles drums were carried in the two axle-mounted chests. The linchpin, with a loop, is visible on the end of the axle. The pointing bar is mounted on the left side of this Gatling; this location provided more elevation than the usual center-mounted aiming bar.

THE GATLING GUN IN CHINA

A Model 1885, 1886 or 1887 Gatling Gun, on a "wheelbarrow" traveling carriage in China. The large wheel made moving the 260-pound Gatling, the tripod and complement of Accles drums somewhat easier over China's poor roads.

The same Gatling, mounted on a metal tripod, ready to fire. The Aiming Bar extends from the breech of the gun. Each chest held four Accles drums, the rear sight,, and the gunner's implements. The "Wheelbarrow Gun" lacked the sales appeal of the "Camel Gun."

THE 1886 PRICE LIST

PRICE LIST

OF THE

GATLING GUN COMPANY

GATLING GUNS.

(STRAIGHT FEED.)

1.00-inch caliber, ten barrels, . . .	$1,800.00
1.00 " " six "	1,600.00
.75, .65, and .55 caliber, ten long barrels,	1,600.00
Musket caliber (.50, .45, .43, .42, &c.), ten long barrels, ...	1,000.00
Musket caliber, ten short barrels, . .	850.00
Musket " five " " .	750.00

(POSITIVE OR ACCLES' FEED.)

Musket caliber, ten long barrels and four feed magazines, ...	1,400.00
Musket caliber, six short barrels and four feed magazines, ...	1,000.00

GUN CARRIAGES, FEED CASES, ETC.

Carriage and Limber for Positive Feed Gun,	$400.00
Carriage and Limber for all other Guns,	300.00
Navy Carriage of steel, iron, and brass (no Limber required), . . .	300.00
Tripod, ...	125.00
Pack Saddle, ...	110.00
Fixture for mounting Gun on gunwale of ship (not required when Navy Carriages are ordered), . . .	100.00
Bed Plate for gunwale of ship, . .	6.00
Straight Feed Cases, .55-inch caliber and larger, ...	2.80
Straight Feed Cases, .50-inch caliber and smaller, ...	2.25
Feed Magazines, ...	40.00

AMMUNITION.

1.00-inch caliber Cartridges, per thousand,					$200.00
.75 "	"	"	"	"	180.00
.65 "	"	"	"	"	170.00
.55 "	"	"	"	"	160.00
Musket	"	"	"	"	22.00

Cartridge shells of all sizes can be re-loaded and used fifty times and upwards.

The prices of Cartridges are subject to change without notice.

PACKING.

Guns of .55-inch caliber and larger, . .	$17.00
Guns of .50-inch caliber and smaller, .	9.00
Carriage and Limber for Gun of 55-inch caliber and larger, . . .	25.00
Carriage and Limber for Musket caliber Gun,	20.00
Tripods, ...	3.00

The Guns are packed in tin-lined boxes, and the packing-boxes for the Carriages and Limbers are hooped.

The above prices are in United States currency, and payment is required in all cases upon rendering the invoice.

All deliveries are made on cars or boat at Hartford, but if desired we will attend to placing the goods on board ship at New York, charging the actual cost therefor.

ALL PREVIOUS PRICES ARE HEREBY REVOKED.

Address,

THE GATLING GUN COMPANY,

HARTFORD, CONNECTICUT,

UNITED STATES OF AMERICA.

HARTFORD, Sept. 1, 1886.

Published by the Gatling Gun Company on September 1, 1886. The ammunition offered in this price list was probably that manufactured by the Union Metallic Cartridge Company, of Bridgeport, Connecticut.

THE MODEL 1889 POLICE GATLING GUN
(Experimental)

This unique .45-70 Model 1889 Police Gatling Gun was announced in the Hartley & Graham catalogue for 1889. The text reads:

> "The above illustration represents the *new and improved Police Gatling Gun*, with six barrels mounted on tripod. In appearance it is somewhat similar to the Accles feed gun, only is of much lighter construction, the barrels being only 12 inches in length and the entire gun and tripod weighing only about 80 pounds. Its small size and weight render it extremely valuable for use in quelling riots, etc., etc."

The aiming bar is short; the simple semi-circular arc serves to control elevation and depression. The tripod has wooden legs with bronze "feet;" the legs are limited in their spread. Production would not begin until 1893, when the design was reintroduced as the Model 1893 Bulldog (Police) Gatling Gun. Even then, no report has been found describing the use of a Police Gatling "in quelling riots, etc., etc."

THE "MODEL 1890" ELECTRIC GATLING GUN

From *The Scientific American*, for November 15, 1890. The Crocker-Wheeler Motor Company of New York City developed this electric firing device at the request of the U.S. Navy. The reported rate of fire was 1,500 rounds per minute. Unlike Gatling's 1893 design, this variation permitted the crank to be used when the clutch of the electric motor was disengaged. Figure 1 is the Gatling being fired by the push of an electric switch. Figure 2 shows the mounting and attachment of the electric motor to the Gatling. The large plate on the front of the Accles Drum bears the Crocker-Wheeler Motor Company data. Figure 3 shows the details of this electric motor.

A HARTLEY & GRAHAM PRICE LIST
FOR GATLING GUNS AND ACCESSORIES

PRICE LIST
OF
GATLING GUNS AND AMMUNITION.

GATLING GUNS.

(STRAIGHT FEED.)

1.00-inch calibre, ten barrels			$1,800.00
.75- " " ten "			1,600.00
.65- " " ten "			1,600.00
.55- " " ten "			1,500.00
Musket " (50, 45, 43, 42, &c.) ten long barrels			1,000.00
Musket calibre, ten short barrels			850.00
Musket " five " "			750.00

(POSITIVE OR ACCLES' FEED.)

Musket calibre, ten long barrels and four feed magazines	1,400.00
Musket calibre, six long barrels and four feed magazines	

GUN CARRIAGES, FEED CASES, ETC.

Carriage and Limber for Positive Feed Gun	400.00
Carriage and Limber for all other Guns	300.00
Navy Carriage of Steel, Iron and Brass, (no Limber required)	300.00
Tripod	125.00
Pack Saddle	110.00
Fixtures for mounting gun on gunwale of ship (not required when Navy Carriages are ordered)	100.00
Bed-Plate for Gunwale of ship	5.00
Straight Feed Cases, 55-inch calibre and larger	2.80
Straight Feed Cases, 50-inch calibre and smaller	2.25
Feed Magazines	37.50

AMMUNITION.

1.00-inch calibre Cartridges, pr thousand	$200.00
.75- " " " " "	180.00
.65- " " " " "	170.00
.55- " " " " "	160.00
Musket	24.00

Cartridge Shells of all sizes can be reloaded and used fifty times and upwards.

The prices of Cartridges are subject to change without notice.

PACKING.

Guns of 55-inch calibre and larger	$17.00
Guns of 50-inch calibre and smaller	9.00
Carriage and Limber for Gun of 55-inch calibre and larger	25.00
Carriage and Limber for Musket calibre Gun	20.00
Tripods	3.00

The Guns are packed in tin-lined boxes, and the packing boxes for the Cartridges and Limbers are hooped.

The above prices are in United States currency, and payment is requested in all cases upon rendering the invoice.

All previous prices are hereby revoked.

This price list, ca.1886–1892, was issued by Harley & Graham of New York City. They were dealers in both sporting and military arms and the export agents for Remington Arms Company and the Union Metallic Cartridge Company. Both of these companies were owned or controlled by Marcellus Hartley.

THE MODEL 1893 GATLING GUN

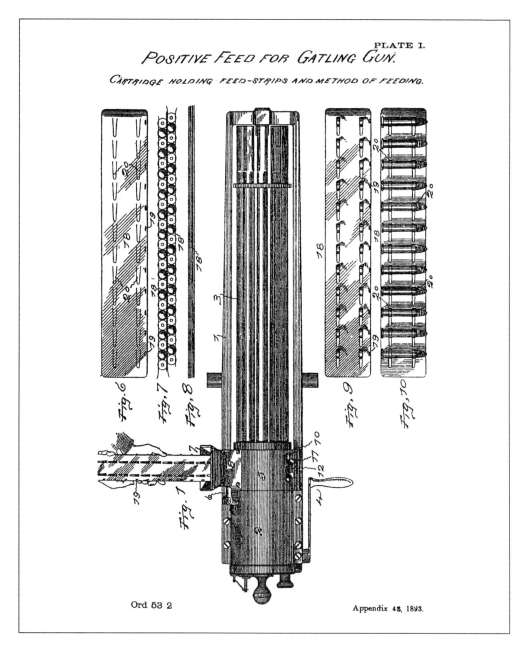

This Gatling Gun introduced the "Positive Feed" strips patented by Broderick and Vankeirs-bilck. Springfield Armory was granted the rights to manufacture these strips. They also retained the right to have these Gatlings altered to accept the Bruce feed. This option was exercised during 1897. Colt's was paid $200 per gun to alter the 18 Model 1893 Gatlings to the proven Bruce feed.

THE MODEL 1893 GATLING GUN

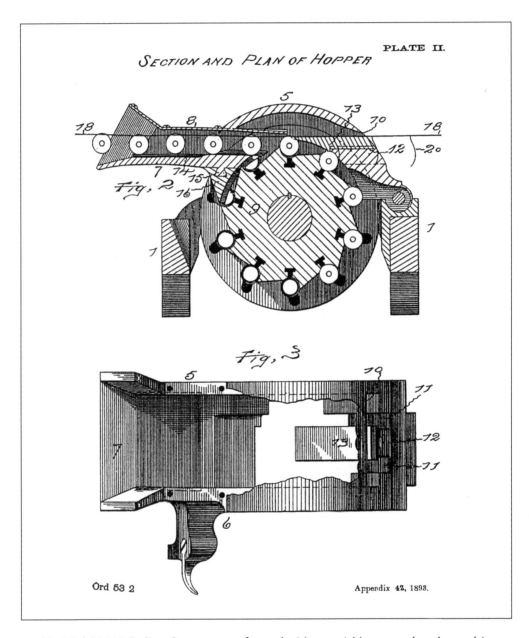

The Model 1893 Gatling Gun was manufactured with a special hopper and ratchet to drive the "Positive Feed" strips holding the .30-40 ammunition. Springfield Armory received complaints about these feed strips beginning in 1894, the year the Model 1893 Gatling Guns were delivered and placed in service. Colt's blamed the feed problems on improperly made feed strips from Springfield Armory.

THE MODEL 1893 GATLING GUN

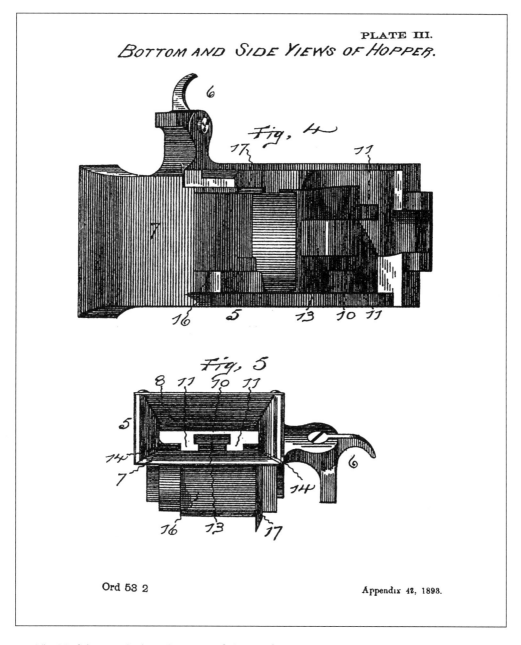

The Model 1893 Gatling Gun was a failure in field service. When additional .30-40 chambered Gatling Guns were ordered in 1895, the Bruce feed was specified. These feed strips had a service life of only three years. The original contract for 18 was the only order placed for Gatlings of the Model 1893 pattern.

THE CONVERTED MODEL 1893 GATLING GUN

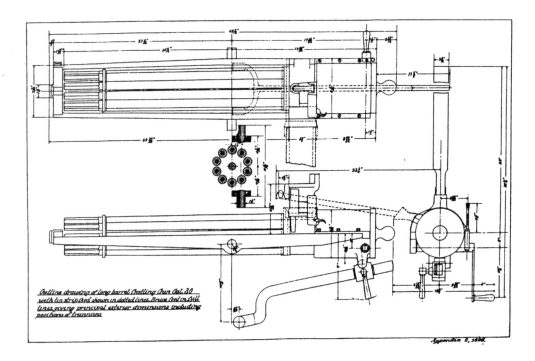

This Springfield Armory drawing from 1896 shows the Model 1893 Gatling Gun altered to accept the Bruce feed on top of the original hopper for the "tin feed strip." Conversion of the 18 Model 1893 Gatlings was completed by June 30, 1897. The original design permitted the feed strip

to enter the Gatling from the left and, when empty, be ejected on the right. The reliable Bruce feed was mounted on top of the Model 1893 hopper. It is shown in solid lines, while the feed strip is shown with dotted lines.

THE MODEL 1893 BULLDOG (POLICE) GATLING GUN

From *The Scientific American* for March 19, 1892. The Hartford Police Department was given a Model 1893 Bulldog (Police) Gatling Gun by either Colt's or the Gatling Gun Company during 1892; this served to introduce this new model. Less than ten are reported to have been manufactured.

THE MODEL 1893 ELECTRIC GATLING GUN

Unlike the Crocker-Wheeler experiment of 1890, R.J. Gatling attached the armature of his electric motor directly to the main shaft. This permitted the complete motor unit to be enclosed within the bronze breech casing of the gun.

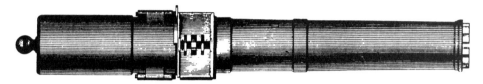

A top view of the assembled Model 1893 Electric Gatling Gun. The mounting plate for the Accles feed drum is visible just ahead of the access port for the bolts. The extended breech jacket protects the electric motor. Because the motor was attached directly to the main shaft, no provision was made for using a crank as an alternative method of operating the gun. The reported rate of fire was 3,000 rounds per minute, twice that of the Crocker-Wheeler adaptation three years earlier.

THE MODEL 1895 GATLING GUN

The Model 1895 Gatling Gun was issued with two patterns of Bruce feeds, the Model 1895 and Model 1897. These feeds were interchangeable; the Model 1897 had minor changes to the grooves that retained the cartridges to improve feeding. This drawing appeared in the 1908 version of the manual.

THE MODEL 1893 ELECTRIC GATLING GUN

WAR DEPARTMENT
OFFICE OF THE CHIEF OF ORDNANCE
WASHINGTON

Hg

In replying refer to No. *37888/3038*

April 18, 1914.

Mr. W. H. Ireland,
    4124 Second Avenue,
    Pittsburgh, Pa.

Mailed APR 18 1914

Sir:

    1.   Referring to your letter without date, received April 16, 1914 (O.O. 37888/3034), requesting information as to the make of gun in this or foreign countries possessing the greatest rapidity of fire, I am instructed by the Chief of Ordnance to inform you that no gun has ever exceeded the rate of fire of the Gatling gun, motor driven. It is understood that with this gun a rate of fire of 3,000 rounds per minute from its ten barrels is possible.

    2.   The greatest rate of fire from a single barrel is possessed by the automatic gun manufactured by the Vickers Company which will fire from the single barrel approximately 800 rounds per minute.

               Respectfully,

               L T HILLMAN

               Major, Ord. Dept., U.S. Army.

This 1914-dated letter from the Chief of Ordnance attests to the 3,000 rounds per minute fired by the Model 1893 Electric Gatling Gun.

THE FIRING CYCLE OF A MODEL 1895 GATLING GUN

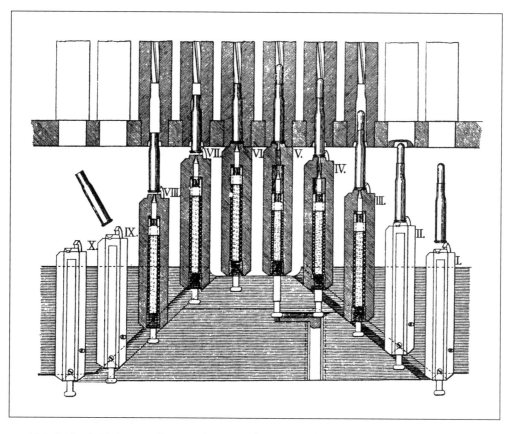

This Springfield Armory diagram shows the firing cycle for a 10-barreled .30-40 Model 1895 Gatling Gun. From right to left, the Gatling is being loaded and fired and the cartridge case extracted. Note the early .30 Krag bullet shown in this drawing.

THE CALIFORNIA NATIONAL GUARD, NAVAL BATTALION
.30-40 ACCLES GUN

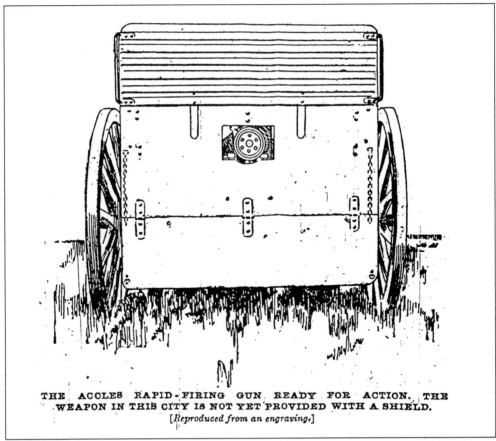

THE ACCLES RAPID-FIRING GUN READY FOR ACTION. THE WEAPON IN THIS CITY IS NOT YET PROVIDED WITH A SHIELD.
[*Reproduced from an engraving.*]

This 6-barrel Accles Gun was delivered to San Francisco on June 1, 1895. It was issued to Company D, Naval Reserve the following day. The shipboard mount and shield were expected in several months. (*San Francisco Call*, June 5, 1895)

THE U.S. NAVY MODEL 6mm ACCLES GUN

These illustrations are from the *Francis Bannerman Catalogue of Military Goods for 1949*. This Accles "machine gun" was advertised for sale as a Gatling Gun. It was ordered in 6mm Lee-Navy caliber, to use the same cartridge as the Model 1895 Lee Navy Rifle manufactured by Winchester. It is unusual, in that it was made with an aluminum barrel jacket. James G. Accles himself described his gun as an "improved Gatling." He moved the crank to the right trunnion to lessen the disturbance of the aim during cranking. The Accles also had a trigger that permitted the gunner to fire "bursts" while his assistant turned the crank continually. This gun was developed after Accles left his employment with the Gatling Gun Company. Is was manufactured, not by Colt's, but by the Driggs Ordnance Company of Washington, D.C. Only a few were ordered by the U.S. Navy about 1896.

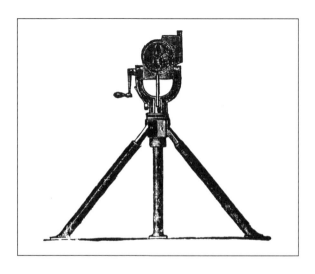

THE FIRING CYCLE OF A MODEL 1903 GATLING GUN

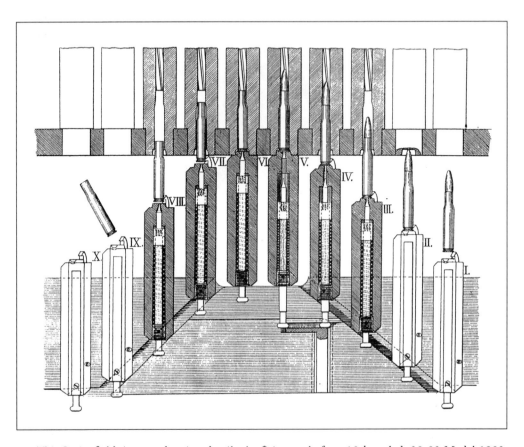

This Springfield Armory drawing details the firing cycle for a 10-barreled .30-03 Model 1903 Gatling Gun. As the barrels rotate, they are loaded, the firing pin "cocked" at positions IV and V, and the gun fires at position VI. The spent cartridge is ejected at position IX. This cycle is the same for all 10-barreled Gatlings.

THE GATLING GUN BATTERY
1910

Indicating that the Gatling Gun was still regarded as "artillery" by the U.S. Army as late as 1910, the manual indicated that a company would be equipped as a "Gatling-gun battery" with the following equipment:

> 6 Gatling Guns, .30-06
> 6 Carriages, for .30-06 Gatling Guns
> 6 Limbers, for machine guns
> 1 Battery Wagon and forge
> 1 Store Wagon
> 1 Spare Wheel
> 9 sets Lead Harness
> 8 sets Wheel Harness
> 17 Harness Sacks

The battery wagon and forge were issued with a complement of tools and cleaning and preservation supplies for six months service in the field.

Gatling Guns were each drawn by four horses, as was the store wagon. The heavier battery wagon required six horses.

Ammunition (.30-06) was distributed as follows:

> 9,900 rounds in each limber
> 1,000 rounds in the "body of the carriage"
> 300 rounds in the "upper trail compartment"

The 1,000 rounds carried in the "body of the carriage" was stored in an iron-bound wooden box. To protect these cartridges from the weather, a canvas cover was fitted on top of the hinged lid. This ammunition chest had two wooden interior partitions.

Several of the component parts of the limber were the same as those for the 3.2" Field Gun. These interchangeable parts were, described in the manual as the doubletree, neck yoke, pole, pole prop and singletree.

Part of the harness issued for field service with the Gatling Gun. The saddle appears to be of the McClellan pattern. A single tree is attached to the draft harness.

THE U.S. ARMY "CAVALRY CART"

This combination field carriage/limber appeared on the U.S. military scene with the Model 1874 Camel Gun. The manual suggested the use of a single "horse for good roads, two horses for bad" roads. This was the lightest field carriage in United States Army service.

The Cavalry Cart mounted Gatling ready to fire. Each wooden chest held 24 Model 1874 Magazines (960 rounds); a third chest was suspended beneath the axle of the cart. This held 2,000 rounds of .45-70 ammunition and the gunner's implements.

THE ALL-METAL FIELD CARRIAGE
MODEL 1884

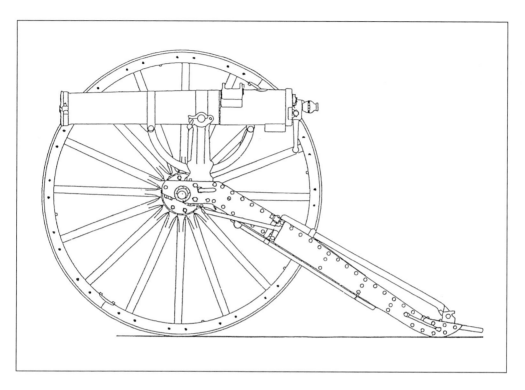

  This "all-metal" field carriage was constructed by Watervliet Arsenal during late 1884. It was designed for use with the Model 1883 Gatling Gun fitted for the Accles feed. As was the standard U.S. Army practice, Archibald wheels, with wooden spokes and felloes, were used. No provision was made for filling the Accles drums, a rather slow process. The carriages was designed by Lt. W.B. Gordon of the Ordnance Department. A number were rushed into production. Four were made with the experimental hinged handspike in the illustration. This carriage, complete with chests and implements, weighed 594 pounds. The Gatling Gun added another 245 pounds. Four Accles feeds were carried in the axle-mounted chests; they weighed 16 pounds each. (From the 1885 manual)

THE METAL FIELD CARRIAGE
for the
GATLING GUN, MODELS 1895, 1900 and 1903

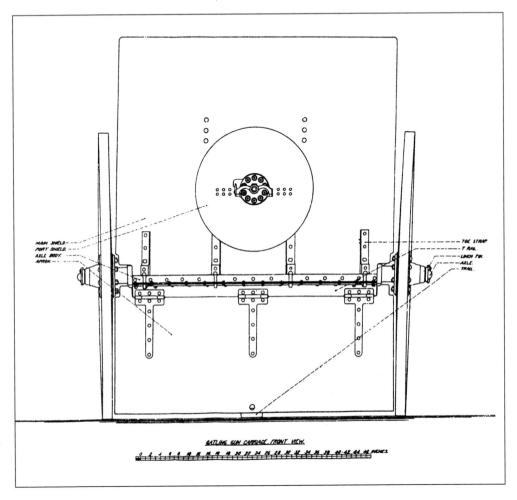

A front view of the "all-metal" field carriage issued with .30-06 caliber Gatling Guns, Models of 1895, 1900 and 1903. The "apron," or lower shield, folded up below the Gatling to increase the ground clearance while traveling. The upper shield was made in the form of an arc; it was 46" tall and filled the 57" between the wheels of the field carriage. The flat lower shield was 22.35" tall and 57" wide. Both were made of hardened steel, .2" thick. The circular shield mounted on the frame of the Gatling Gun was 24" in diameter. It was slightly dished. The 6.1" diameter gun port was cut away on the right side "enough at the proper point to permit aiming." The three-part shield protected the gunner from small arms fire. If the field carriage became damaged, it was to be returned to Rock Island Arsenal for repairs. This pattern shield was an improvement over the earlier type, which hindered movement of the Gatling Gun. (From the 1910 manual)

THE METAL FIELD CARRIAGE
for the
GATLING GUN, MODELS 1895, 1900 and 1903

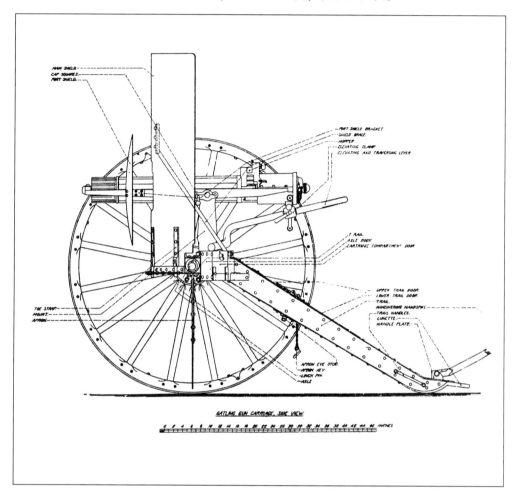

A side view of the "all-metal" field carriage issued with .30-06 caliber Gatling Guns, Models of 1895, 1900 and 1903. The curvature of the main shield and the dished gun shield are shown. The retainer for the "apron" while traveling dangles below the trail on a chain. The pointing bar has undergone a name change; it is now the "elevating and traversing lever." This "all-metal" carriage used the Archibald pattern wheels (wooden spokes and felloes) adopted earlier. A hinged handspike has been fitted to the lower end of the trail. This pattern handspike was adopted by the United Kingdom in 1871. (From the 1910 manual)

119

THE GATLING GUN LIMBER
(Early Model)

A rear view of the early pattern limber for the .50-70 and .45-70 Gatling Gun. The loaded magazines, either .50-70 straight feed or .45-70 gravity feed, were carried in the limber chest. On the march, two gunners rode on the chest; the limber towed the Gatling Gun.

To soften the ride on the limber (which had no springs), canvas-covered cushions were issued. They were filled with horsehair as padding. The cushion measured 27" x 46" x 2¼".

THE GATLING GUN LIMBER
(MODEL 1883)

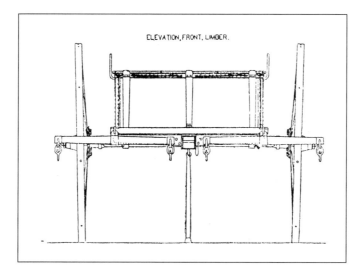

A front view of the Model 1883 Gatling Gun Limber, with a steel ammunition chest. This chest held the Accles Drums; it also provided a seat for the gunners while the Gatling was being transported. The wheels were the Archibald pattern. The spokes and felloes were quickly replaceable in the event of damage.

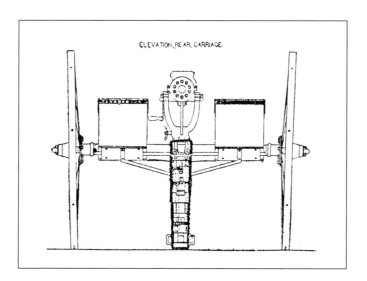

A front (muzzle) view of the Model 1883 Gatling Gun, on the standard steel and bronze field carriage. The ammunition chests on either side of the Gatling held Accles Drums and the standard issue gunner's implements. The field carriage wheels were interchangeable with those of the Model 1883 Limber.

THE GATLING GUN LIMBER
used with
MODELS 1895, 1900 and 1903

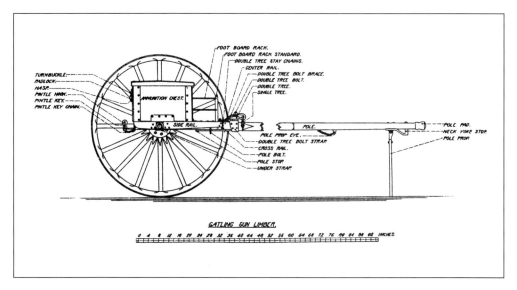

This pattern limber was adopted for use with all .30-06 caliber Gatling Guns. These were the Models 1895 and 1900 (converted from .30-40) and the Model 1903 (converted from .30-03). It was also used with the Model 1883 Gatling Gun chambered for the .45-70 cartridge. The ammunition chest, neck yoke, pole and spokes and felloes of the wheels were the only wooden components. There were three metal footboards in front of the ammunition chest on the latest design limber. Earlier models had only two; Rock Island Arsenal undertook a program to convert these early limbers to the three footboard pattern. The ammunition chest was moved to the rear and the third footboard added. Rock Island Arsenal was also the repair site for limbers damaged beyond field repair from spare parts on hand. The ammunition chest was divided into three compartments; the lid was covered with canvas "painted to render it waterproof." Carried in this chest, in cardboard boxes of 20, were 9,900 rounds of .30-06 ammunition. An additional 1,200 rounds was carried on the field carriage for the Gatling Gun. The illustration is from the 1910 manual.

THE NAVAL BULWARK GATLING GUN MOUNT

This pre-1876 10-barrel long Gatling Gun is shown mounted on the bulwark of a sailing ship. The extreme depression of the Gatling would indicate that it was ready to repel boarders. The 1905 Bannerman catalogue advises that, "With the aid of ship's carpenter can be readily mounted as desired. Can also be mounted in the ship tops or in launch." This "mount" is simply the yoke assembly removed from an army field carriage!

THE U.S. NAVY MODEL 1874 LIMBER

This limber was adopted by the U.S. Navy for use with the Model 1874 Gatling Gun with ten long barrels. This .50-70 caliber Gatling was designed to use Broadwell Drums. The three chests on the limber each held a Broadwell Drum and a supply of cartridges to be used in refilling the feed device. With the two chests on the gun carriage, a total of five drums were available for the Gatling Gun. A portion of the trail of the carriage for the Gatling Gun is shown, attached to the pintle hook of the limber.

THE AMMUNITION BOX

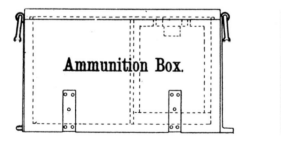
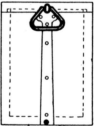

A total of five of these interchangeable ammunition chests were issued with each U.S. Navy long-barreled .50-70 Gatling Gun. Each held a Broadwell Drum in a protective compartment and cartridges to fill it. For use in landing boats, the chests could be removed from the carriage or limber and placed near the Gatling Gun in the bow of the boat.

THE U.S. NAVY MODEL 1874 CAISSON BOX

Three of these "Caisson Boxes" were mounted on the limber ("caisson") for the short-barreled Model 1874 .50-70 Gatling Gun. Two more were on the field carriage for the Gatling. Each box held a dozen straight-feed magazines; each magazine held 40 rounds of .50-70 ammunition. This system permitted 2,400 rounds to be carried with the Gatling when it was accompanied by the limber. A reserve supply of ammunition was to be carried in the ship's boats used by the landing party. From the 1875 U.S. Navy manual.

THE U.S. NAVY CARRIAGE
FOR "SMALL" GATLING GUNS

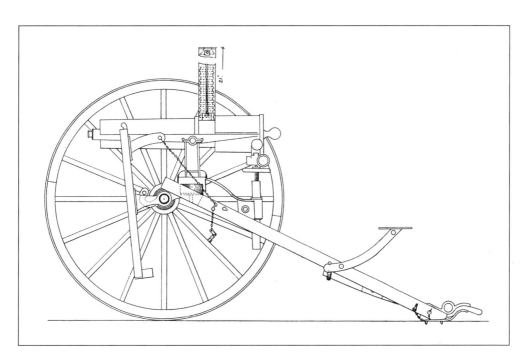

This "all-metal" carriage was developed for use with their short-barreled ("small") .50-70 Gatling Guns during 1874 or 1875. In spite of the "all-metal" designation, the spokes and felloes of the wheels were wooden. The empty racks to hold the ammunition chests are tipped forward in this drawing from the 1875 manual. This version used tinned feed cases instead of the Broadwell Drums.

U.S. NAVY DECK MOUNTS

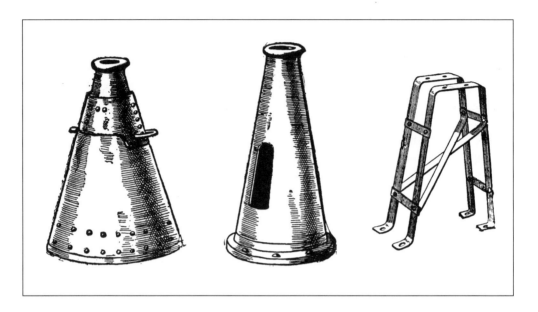

Three patterns of deck mounts used by the U.S. Navy for Gatling Guns. The two "cone" or "pedestal" mounts had steel bodies with brass sockets at the top to accept the yoke of the Gatling Gun and brass flanges at the base to bolt the mount to the deck. The height of the riveted steel body pattern is 37". The rolled steel body pattern is 38" tall. A tool compartment is provided in this "British pattern" mount. The "cage" pattern mount was made of wrought iron. A mounting plate to accept the yoke of the Gatling Gun had to be bolted to the top of this style mount. All three patterns saw service with the U.S. Navy during the Spanish-American War (1898). After the war, they were sold as surplus to Francis Bannerman of New York City.

BRITISH NAVY "FIGHTING TOP" MOUNT

British sailors man a Gatling Gun mounted in a fighting top of a frigate, the H.M.S. *Shah*, off Ylo, Peru. This Gatling played an important part in the naval engagement with the Peruvian ship, the *Huascar*, on May 29, 1877. This Gatling was mounted in the foretop and swept the decks clear of Peruvian sailors. Interestingly, the *Huascar* was built by Laird in Birkenhead, England, for the Peruvian navy. Of course, the Royal Navy's Gatling Gun was manufactured by Sir William Armstrong & Company, in Newcastle-on-Tyne, England.

A GATLING ARMED POWER LAUNCH

During 1907, Francis Bannerman, the New York City military surplus dealer, purchased a new power launch to carry military goods to and from his island arsenal in the Hudson River. He armed it with a surplus U.S. Army Gatling Gun and offered it for sale on the back cover of his 1907 catalogue. The "Polopel" was described as being 30 feet long, 10 feet wide and had a draft of only 3½ feet when laden with 10 tons of freight. It was powered by an 11-horsepower Lathrop gasoline engine. Speed was rated at eight knots. Suitable as a government freight tender or coastal patrol vessel, the "Polopel" was offered "for sale with gun fully equipped at bargain. Price quoted upon application."

HOW TO LOAD GATLING GUN MAGAZINES
from various U.S. manuals

The Broadwell Drum:

Invert the drum, unlock it, turn the bottom plate until the hole comes directly over a compartment, raise the follower weight with the left hand and fill in the cartridges regularly, the bullets being placed next to the centre [center] of the drum, letting the weight down slowly until the compartment is full. Repeat the operation until all are filled [400 rounds]. Take care to turn the bottom plate so that it can be locked before placing the drum upright again.

The Model 1874 Feed Case:

Invert the case, draw back the [cartridge retaining] spring, and slip a cartridge between it and the wall of the case. This keeps the mouth of the case open and free to receive the cartridges. Place the case between the knees, with the spring to the front, raise the follower weight with the left hand, and fill in the cartridges regularly, with the bullets to the left. Lower the left hand gradually until the case is full [40 rounds]. Withdraw the cartridge from under the spring.

The Accles Drum:

To fill the magazine, grasp it with the left hand, having the mouth at a slight downward angle, turn the propeller towards you with the forefinger of the left hand, at the same time using the right hand to fill the magazine with cartridges [104 rounds of .45-70 ammunition].

MAGAZINES AND FEED DEVICES
FOR AMERICAN GATLING GUNS

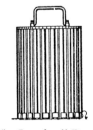

The Broadwell Drum,
adopted in 1871,
.50-70 or .45-70.
To hold 400 rounds.

The Model 1874 Gravity
Feed Magazine, .45-70.
Tin and bronze construction,
to hold 40 rounds.

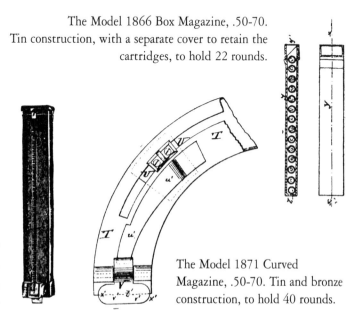

The Model 1866 Box Magazine, .50-70.
Tin construction, with a separate cover to retain the
cartridges, to hold 22 rounds.

The Model 1871 Curved
Magazine, .50-70. Tin and bronze
construction, to hold 40 rounds.

MAGAZINES AND FEED DEVICES
FOR AMERICAN GATLING GUNS

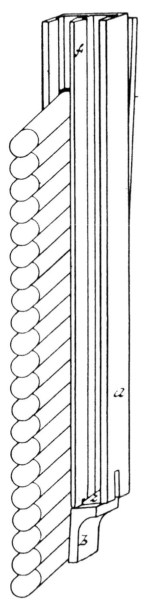

The Bruce Feed, adopted in 1881, .45-70, .30-40, .30-03, or .30-06. This was the longest lasting feed in service with the Gatling Gun. Several models exist, including two for the .30-40 cartridge, i.e., Model 1895 and Model 1897.

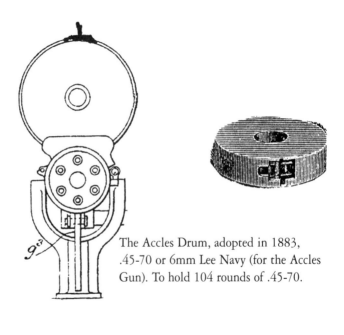

The Accles Drum, adopted in 1883, .45-70 or 6mm Lee Navy (for the Accles Gun). To hold 104 rounds of .45-70.

The Model 1893 Strip Feed, .30-40, replaced in 1897 by the Bruce Feed as originally adopted in 1881.

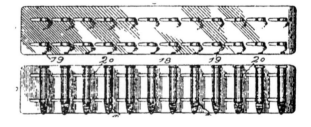

IMPLEMENTS ISSUED WITH THE
MODEL 1874 GATLING GUN

Rear Guide Nut Wrench, top and side views

Brass Wiping (Cleaning) Rod

Shell Driver
(used to remove a headless shell from the chamber)

Pin Wrench

Adjusting Screw Wrench (used to set head space)

T Screwdriver

Lock Screwdriver (used to strip bolts)

Small Screwdriver

Clamp for Worm Gear (gear puller)

These implements (appendages) were issued with each Model 1874 .45-70 Gatling Gun. They were the same for either the long- or short-barreled version. The total cost, in 1875, of a complete set of implements for one gun was $16.92. Basically, the same tools were issued as late as 1917 in United States Army service.

IMPLEMENTS AND ACCESSORIES
FOR AMERICAN ARMY GATLING GUNS

1885: The following were issued with the Model 1883 Gatling on the Model 1884 "all-metal" field carriage and stowed in the axle mounted chests for the Accles feed drums:

Left Chest	Right Chest:	On the trail:
2 Accles feed drums	2 Accles feed drums	1 Aiming bar
1 cam extractor	1 crank handle	1 cleaning rod
1 riveting hammer	1 pin drift	
1 oil can	1 bolt tool	
1 screw-wrench	1 pin-wrench	
1 rear sight, left side	1 screw driver	
	1 T screwdriver	
	1 rear sight, right side	

1908: The "Accessories and Tools" issued with each gun were:

2 Bruce feed guides	1 shell driver	1 pointing lever,
1 brass wiping rod	1 lock [bolt] screwdriver	complete
1 T screwdriver	1 small screwdriver	
1 rear guide nut wrench	1 cascabel wrench	
1 lever axis pin nut wrench	1 pin wrench	
1 drift	1 crank handle and pin	

The following spare parts were issued with each gun:

1 lock [bolt], complete	1 mainspring
2 extractors	2 extractor screws
1 firing pin nut	1 firing pin bushing screw

1917: The "Tools and Accessories" issued with each Model 1895, 1900 and 1903 .30-06 Gatling Gun included the following:

2 Bruce feed guides	1 pin wrench	1 tarpaulin,12' x 12'
1 rear guide nut wrench	1 cascabel plate wrench	
1 drift	1 shell driver	
1 lock screwdriver	1 small screwdriver	
1 lever axis pin nut wrench	1 T screwdriver	
1 oil can	1 cleaning rod, brass	

If the field carriages had linchpin washers with loops for attaching drag ropes, a pair of drag ropes would be "furnished for each carriage upon request."

IMPLEMENTS AND ACCESSORIES
FOR AMERICAN NAVY GATLING GUNS

1875: In the Spare Article Box, mounted beneath the gun:

1 screwdriver	1 assembling rest
1 wrench for barrel shaft	1 clamp for worm gear
1 wrench and pin for casing screws	1 heaver for casing screws
1 rear guide nut wrench	1 bolt cylinder wrench
1 bolt, complete	1 mallet
1 oil can	1 box or can of lubricant for cartridges

Spare Parts:

2 coil springs for firing pins	2 coil springs for locking ring
1 clamp, to hold the bolt	1 wrench for the lock bolt
1 crutch for the traversing gear	1 extractor
1 firing pin	4 lock butt screws
4 extractor screws	1 screwdriver
2 washers and linchpin	

In the haversack:

1 sponge	1 file, half round
1 brush, for cleaning rod	1 file, flat
Wiping "stuff" (tow)	1 bolt, complete, to be taken from the Spare Article Box when preparing for action

On the carriage:

1 cleaning rod	1 shell driver
1 bore scraper, to remove leading	1 fire bucket, on the pintle hook

Each Gatling Gun crew member was armed personally with a cutlass and handgun. The haversack (above) was worn by the No. 1 crewman, "from the left shoulder to the right side."

THE 1875 INSPECTOR'S MANUAL

Rules for the Inspection

OF

ARMY REVOLVERS

AND

GATLING GUNS.

PREPARED UNDER THE DIRECTION OF
LIEUT. COL. J. G. BENTON,
Commanding National Armory,
—BY—
CAPT. J. P. FARLEY, ORD. DEPT.

NATIONAL ARMORY:
SPRINGFIELD, MASS.
1875

The title page of the 1875 U.S. Army inspector's manual. This manual was written to cover the acceptance of Model 1874 Gatling Guns, Colt Single Action Army Revolvers and the Smith & Wesson Schofield Revolver. Proofing, inspection, test firing, disassembly and reassembly are all detailed. The illustrated manual has 30 pages.

THE 1875 U.S. NAVY MANUAL

INSTRUCTIONS

FOR

USE AND CARE

OF

GATLING GUNS.

COMPiLED

BY

COMMANDER J. D. MARVIN.

—————

1875.

The front cover of the U.S. Navy manual issued during 1875 on the Model 1874 Gatling Gun. This manual includes "gun drill" field carriages, nomenclature, use, accuracy, etc. The feed device then in service was the Broadwell drum.

THE 1886 U.S. ARMY MANUAL

DEPARTMENT OF PRACTICAL MILITARY INSTRUCTION.

ARTILLERY EXERCISES

CLASS A.

DESCRIPTION AND SERVICE OF

MACHINE GUNS,

Gardner Gun, Hotchkiss Revolving Cannon, Hotchkiss 1.65
inch B. L. Mountain Gun, 0.45 inch Gatling
Guns, Old and New Models.

BY

JOHN H. CALEF,

Captain 2nd Artillery.

FORT MONROE, VA.

PRINTED AT THE

UNITED STATES ARTILLERY SCHOOL.

1886.

The title page of the 1886 U.S. Army manual for "Machine Guns." This manual covered all "light artillery" in service at the time. The "Old Model" Gatlings were those purchased prior to 1883; the Model 1883 Gatling, with the Accles Feed, was described as the "New Model."

THE 1908 MANUAL

THE 1908 MANUAL

No. 1757

NOMENCLATURE AND DESCRIPTION

OF THE

GATLING GUN .30 CALIBER

MODELS OF 1895 AND 1900

NOVEMBER 28, 1896
REVISED JUNE 23, 1908

WASHINGTON
GOVERNMENT PRINTING OFFICE
1908

The title page of the 1908 manual. A total of 250 were printed; they were serial numbered on the front cover and on the back of this page. No. 245 was received at the Sandy Hook Proving Ground (NJ) on April 26, 1916. The manual consisted of 18 pages plus seven folding plates at the back. The Gatling Guns described were conversions to .30-06 from .30-40 contract arms. In addition to the Gatling, Bruce feeds of the Models 1895 and 1897 were described, as well as accessories and tools.

CARTRIDGES FOR GATLING GUNS

IN UNITED STATES SERVICE

Size or Caliber:	Type(s):	Ill. Number(s):
1" Long and Short	Ball, Canister	1, 2
.58 Musket, with steel carrier	Minie ball	5
.58 Rimfire	Ball	6
.50-70-450	Ball, Blank	8
.45-70-500	Ball, Accles Feed Blank	9
.45-70-405	Ball, Blank	10
.30-40	Ball, Blank	22
.30-03	Ball, Blank	23
.30-06	Ball, Blank	24
6mm Lee Navy	Ball	25

IN FOREIGN TRIALS AND SERVICE

In Argentine service:	11mm Spanish, .75 caliber, 1"	17, 3, 1
In Austrian trials:	.42 Berdan, .50-70	19, 8
In Baden trials:	.50-70	8
In Bolivian service:	11mm Spanish	17
In British service:	.45 Gatling, .450 Machine Gun, .450/.577, .450 Indian Service, Ball & Blank, .65" Gatling	11, 12, 13, 14, 4
In Canadian service:	As for Britain	
In Chilean service:	11mm Spanish	17
In Danish trials:	1", 11.45mm Rimfire, .42 Berdan	1, 2, 15, 19
In Danish service:	8mm Danish	21
In Dutch service:	11.3mm Beaumont	16
In Egyptian service:	11mm Egyptian	18
In French service and trials:	.50-70, 1"	8, 1, 2
In Guatemalan service:	11mm Spanish	17
In Italian service:	10.35mm Vetterli	20
In Mexican service:	11mm Spanish	17
In Montenegrin service:	.42 Berdan	19
In Moroccan service:	11mm Egyptian?	18
In Peruvian service	11mm Spanish	17
In Prussian trials:	.50-70, 1"	8, 1, 2
In Rumanian trials:	.50-70?	8
In Russian service:	.42 Berdan	19
In Spanish Service:	11mm Spanish	17
In Swedish trials::	1" ?	1, 2
In Swiss service:	1" Ball & Canister	1, 2
In Tunisian service:	1mm Egyptian ?	18
In Turkish service:	.58 Turkish Snider	7

The above cartridges are illustrated on the following pages, and identified by the Illustration Number.

CARTRIDGES FOR GATLING GUNS

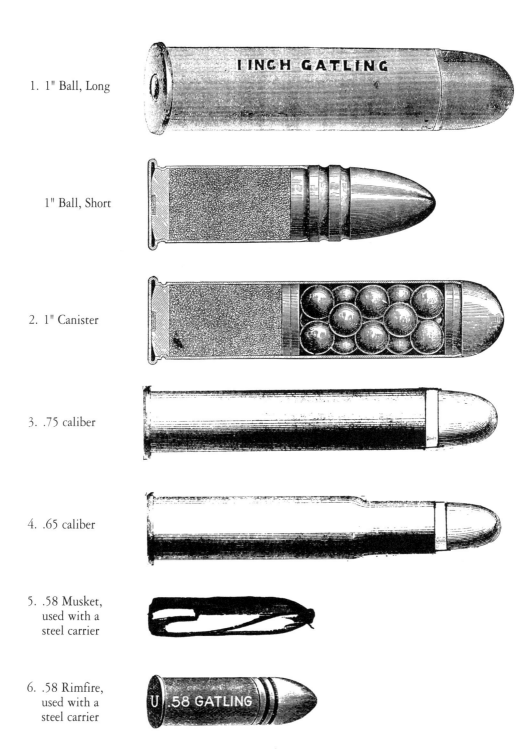

1. 1" Ball, Long

1" Ball, Short

2. 1" Canister

3. .75 caliber

4. .65 caliber

5. .58 Musket,
   used with a
   steel carrier

6. .58 Rimfire,
   used with a
   steel carrier

CARTRIDGES FOR GATLING GUNS

7. .58 Turkish Snider

8. .50-70-450

9. .45-70-500

.45-70 Accles Feed Blank

10. .45-70-405

.45-70 Government Blank

11. .45 Gatling

12. .45 Indian Service

13. .450 Machine Gun

14. .450/.577 (Rifle Chamber)

CARTRIDGES FOR GATLING GUNS

15. 11.45mm Danish Rimfire

16. 11.3mm Beaumont

17. 11mm Spanish

18. 11mm Egyptian

19. .42 Berdan

20. 10.35mm Vetterli

21. 8mm Danish

22. .30-40

.30-40 Blank

23. .30-03

CARTRIDGES FOR GATLING GUNS

24. .30-06

25. 6mm Lee Navy

NOTE: All drawings are approximately 80% actual size.

BIBLIOGRAPHY

Army & Navy Journal	Various issues.
Bannerman, Francis	*Catalogues*, New York, NY, various years.
Behn, Jack	*.45-70 Rifles*, Stackpole Co., Harrisburg, PA, 1956.
Berk, Joseph	*The Gatling Gun, 19th Century Machine Gun To 21st Century Vulcan*, Paladin Press, Boulder, CO, 1991.
British Government	Patent Office
Broad Arrow	Various issues, London, England
Chinn, George M., Lt. Col., USMC	*The Machine Gun*, Bureau of Ordnance, U.S. Navy, Washington, D.C. 1951.
Church, William C.	"American Arms and Ammunition," *Scribner's Monthly*, No. 19, 1880.
Danish Government	Correspondence.
English, Adrian J.	*Armed Forces of Latin America*, Jane's Publishing Co., London, England, 1984.
Eriksen, Egon	"The Gatling Gun" in *Four Studies on History of Arms*, Tojhusmuseets, Copenhagen, Denmark, 1963.
Farrow, Edward S.	*Farrow's Military Encyclopedia*, Military-Naval Publishing Co., New York, NY, 1895.
Fuller, Stephen L.	*United States Martial and Collectors Arms,* Military Arms Research Service, San Jose, CA, 1982.
Gardner, Robert E.	*Small Arms Makers*, Bonanza Books, New York, NY, 1958.
Gatling Gun Company	Advertising, various years, Hartford, CT.
Greener, W.W.	*Modern Breech Loaders Sporting and Military*, Cassell, Petter, and Galpin, London, England, no date.
Guatemalan Government	Correspondence.
Hartley & Graham	Advertising, various years, New York, NY.
Hughes, James B., Jr.	*Mexican Military Arms*, 1866–1967, Deep River Armory, Inc., Houston, TX, 1968.
Illustrated London News	London, England, March 23, 1867.
Kroulik, A. Raymond	Correspondence: Argentine usage.
Lugs, Jaroslav	*Handfuerwaffen*, Deutscher Militarverlag, Berlin, East Germany, 1962.
New York Herald	New York, NY, November 7, 1897.
Norton, Charles B., Brig. Gen.	*American Inventions and Improvements in Breech-Loading Small Arms*, James R. Osgood & Co., Boston, MA, 1882.
San Francisco Call	San Francisco, CA, June 5, 1895.
Scientific American	New York, NY, various issues.
Sellers, Frank M.	"American Gunsmiths," *The Gun Room Press*, Highland Park, NJ, 1983.
Serven, James E.	*Colt Firearms, 1836–1958*, privately published, Santa Ana, CA, 1958.
Stephenson, E. Frank, Jr.	*Gatling, A Photographic Rememberence*, Meherrin River Press, Murfreesboro, NC, 1993.

Sutherland, Robert Q.
and R.L. Wilson

The Book of Colt Firearms, privately published Kansas City, MO, 1971.

Taylerson, A.W.F.

The Revolver, 1865–1888, Crown Publishers, Inc., New York, NY, 1966.

United States Government

Manuals, various years
Patent Office
Report of the Chief or Ordnance, various years
Archives, War and Navy Departments

von Ellger, Karl

Contemporary Military Firearms, 1868.

Wahl, Paul and Donald R. Toppel

The Gatling Gun, Arco Publishing Co., New York, NY, 1965.

Wilhelm, Thomas, Capt.

A Military Dictionary, L.R. Hammersly & Co., Philadelphia, PA, 1881.

Other printed sources and correspondence resulted in data for and history of the Gatling Guns included herein. Because this began as a "notebook" for the author's reference, not all sources were properly recorded through the years it took to assemble this work. If a work, published or unpublished, was used and not listed above, I take this opportunity to say thank you and apologize for my oversight in not properly recording your assistance.

Jim Hughes
Houston, Texas
U.S.A.

INDEX

A Fine Selection of Civil War Titles

CIVIL WAR SMALL ARMS OF THE U.S. NAVY AND MARINE CORPS
by John D. McAulay. This book covers each of the war years in surprising detail, listing specific weapons used on specific ships and in specific engagements. The variety of weapons covered is amazing. Sailors and Marines fought in countless land battles, river actions and skirmishes where small arms played a crucial part in the action. 186 pp., 216 photos, 8.5" x 11".
Hardcover • **$39.00 + p/h**

BURNSIDE BREECH LOADING CARBINES
by Edward A. Hull. This important volume presents a detailed analysis and a model-by-model study of this popular Civil War cavalry arm. This affordable book contains all kinds of information about Burnsides that is unavailable in any other source. Black & white photos, 95 pp., 7" x 9.5". Hardcover • **$16.00 + p/h**

SHARPSHOOTER: Hiram Berdan, His Famous Sharpshooters and their Sharps Rifles
by Wiley Sword. The story of the inventor, his men and the innovative weapon they used. No collector of Civil War firearms will want to miss this book, which is written by one of the most famous and successful authors. 125 pp., 7" x 9.5".
Hardcover • **$18.00 + p/h**

FIREPOWER FROM ABROAD
The Confederate Enfield and the LeMat Revolver
The British-made Enfield rifle was so valued by the South during the Civil War that blockade runners cargoed shipments right up to the last days of the war. Another weapon with strong romantic and historical attachments to the South was the LeMat revolver. Chronicled on these pages is the story of just how these weapons reached the Confederate market — a story rich in international intrigue and details about the weapons themselves. As a bonus, information regarding a variety of other Confederate small arms is presented within the appendices. 120 pp., 7" x 9.5".
Hardcover • **$23.00 + p/h**

CIVIL WAR CARTRIDGE BOXES OF THE UNION INFANTRYMAN
by Paul Johnson. There were four patterns of infantry cartridge boxes used by Union forces during the Civil War. Quoting original Ordnance Department letters, the author describes the development and subsequent pattern changes to these cartridge boxes that were made throughout the rifle-musket percussion era. 175+ photos, 352 pp., 7" x 10".
Hardcover • **$45.00 + p/h**

CIVIL WAR BREECH LOADING RIFLES
by John D. McAulay. Although only about 35,000 of these rifles were purchased by the Union during the Civil War, their effect was enormous. All the major breech loading rifles of the Civil War — and most, if not all, of the obscure types — are detailed, illustrated and set in their historical context. 144 pp., 8.5" x 11". Softcover • **$15.00 + p/h**

AMERICAN SOCKET BAYONETS & SCABBARDS
by Robert M. Reilly. The standard guide to socket bayonets, with hundreds of examples illustrated and explained. Covers from Colonial times through after the Civil War. This book is especially good at helping you to identify unknown examples. The illustrations show the markings and details that you need to look for. 208 pp., 9" x 12". Hardcover • **$45.00 + p/h**

CIVIL WAR PISTOLS OF THE UNION
by John D. McAulay. Union handguns of the War between the States, including government procurement information, issue details and historical background. Also covered are Union pistols used by Confederates, with specific details. This is one of the hottest collecting fields today, and McAulay's guide is the standard reference. Black & white photos. 166 pp., 8.5" x 11".
Softcover • **$24.00** Hardcover • **$36.00 + p/h**

CIVIL WAR ARMS MAKERS & THEIR CONTRACTS
Huge reprint of the famous Holt-Owen Commission report on Ordnance and Ordnance Stores, 1862. Contains an unbelievable wealth of details about more than 100 manufacturers and suppliers of Union guns, pistols, swords, accoutrements and cannon. Over 600 pages! A maker's index helps you to find the information you need. 6" x 9". Hardcover • **$39.50 + p/h**

CIVIL WAR ARMS PURCHASES AND DELIVERIES
The single most quoted source of information about Civil War weapons. Many authors have called it the "bible" of Civil War arms research. Also known as "Executive Document #99," this massive publication is a comprehensive list of every weapons purchase made by the Union. Items covered include muskets, carbines, swords, pistols, ammunition, bayonets, cannon, accoutrements and more. Each entry lists the contractor's name, the size of the order, the date of the purchase, the price, the specifications of the weapon, the date of the original contract and the date of actual payment — all taken from the original government ledgers. 312 pps., 6" x 9". Hardcover. **$39.50 + p/h**

CARBINES OF THE U.S. CAVALRY, 1861–1905
by John D. McAulay. This book covers the entire crucial period stretching from the beginning of the Civil War to the end of the cavalry carbine era in 1905. Includes the War between the States, the Indian Campaigns, Custer's Last Stand, the Rough Riders in Cuba, the Philippine Insurrection and the Boxer Rebellion — all illustrated with 127 photos. 144 pp., 8.5" x 11". Hardcover • **$35.00 + p/h**

THE AMES SWORD CO., 1829–1935
by John D. Hamilton. A comprehensive history of America's foremost sword manufacturer and arms supplier during the Civil War. In these pages, you will find the complete sweep of the company's production, from small arms to cannon and the finest swords ever produced. 255 pp., 8.5" x 11". Color Section.
Hardcover • **$45.00 + p/h**

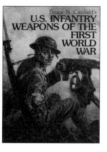

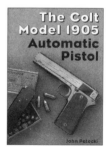

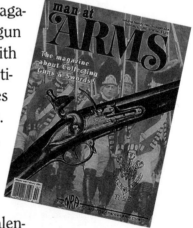